PARTING GIFT

Photo: Florence Homolka

PARTING GIFT

Prose and Poems

John Becker

The Glebe Press
46 Glebe Place
London SW3

1984

Thanks are due to Hilde Halpern, Helen Wolff, Gregory Kenedy, Alan Ross, Jean-Marie Benoist and Tanya Litvinov for their help in making this book possible.

Printed by Unwin Brothers Limited,
The Gresham Press,
Old Woking, Surrey.

Contents

I

II

III

I

YEHUDA AMICHAI

My Friend John

Today I sat down to write about John Becker and his last book. These opening words sound like a ceremonial act rather than a preface or an introduction. I am fully aware of the fact that I have to make a division between John, my friend, and his writings. At the same time I know that both the writer and his works have reached a subtle excellence of performing together. John Becker's personality is constantly felt in these stories. He did not try to hide or to camouflage his characters in a crude way, nor did he turn his creativity into a confessional tour-de-force. John is his stories and the stories are John.

John's house had very much the same personality as his stories, the same intelligent and moving manner of projecting personality into a larger, more objective situation in which others could look and enjoy without entering too much into intimate privacies.

When at a later stage of our friendship, John let me read his yet unpublished stories, I soon found out that each story was actually an additional room in his house as well as each room one more story by John Becker. Stairs leading up and down, doors open or half-open to more rooms hidden or half hidden. Words and walls mixing constantly in their quiet way and always happening at the right time. It seemed to me that this house with his words were like the famous Chinese vase in Rilke's poem which although motionless is constantly moving, turning and turning around.

I have known quite a few authors in my life and it is with some banal wisdom that I can say that all artists use their private lives as background or as foreground for their work, and that all of them turn their personal experience into material for their books or at least into energy supplying matter for their creative process. John did all this in his own original way. He created his stories in a strange space where everything happening seems like real life, yet lighter and more transparent, as if made from a very special material.

His stories, elegant and cool but never cold, are like a heated pool which seems cool on the surface but when you start swimming you can feel the warm currents from underneath. It's an introvert world turned into a surface world without sub-conscious games. I want again to use a phrase of Rilke: *Nirgends, geliebte, wird Welt sein als Innen* (Nowhere, my love, can there be reality but within). The poems – some of them written for children – are made from the very same substance.

After Geneva, published in 1975 by London Magazine Editions, bears all these qualities. I would like to cite from the blurb of this book the following sentences: "At once sophisticated but with an underlying optimism and innocence, John Becker's stories elaborate some of the ambiguities of the American at home and abroad, exploring at the same time the possibilities and limits of romantic love. Each story, with its quick bare dialogue is complete in itself, but together they form a kind of autobiographical novel, sometimes fictional in detail but always true in essence."

The stories in this book, like those in *After Geneva,* are really one story with different titles and changed names. The whole book is like a continent torn by some geological happening into many islands, some smaller, some larger. Each island has kept the characteristics of the mother-continent.

I last saw John who died far from his native America and even farther away from the ancestral world of 19th century German Jews, about a year before his death. We had a peaceful and beautiful lunch. He never talked to me about his health but when he accompanied me to the gate I had the sudden feeling that John felt he would never see me again. Back in my hotel room I sat down and wrote this poem about him:

A Man Marked for Death

A Man marked for death
In his high-walled garden
Put his hand on my shoulders
To bless me with the blessings
Of those marked for death.

Behind him, in the grass
The toys of his grandchild in full light,
The flowers in shade
"Don't forget me." Life passes,
I once heard soldiers' singing
On an open truck passing between hills
I didn't see them but I heard their song
Life passes like this
A man needs to possess the memory-power
Of a waiter. Don't forget to remember.
He brought me to the garden's gate,
And there we separated. He returned
To his marked house.
The heavy decorated door
Closed slowly, with a sophisticated buzz,
Behind me and turned me into
A man of outer space.

The Roman Years

I knew John Becker for around thirty years and although in recent times we saw little of each other (after moving to London his visits to Italy, especially Rome, became increasingly rare and reluctant) I think I can say that our friendship survived the decades intact, despite distance and a difference in age.

It was after his transfer to London that we embarked on a regular, if infrequent, correspondence. This ceased abruptly three years ago with his last letter dated March 29, 1980. From then on he used the phone to keep in touch or to ask the precise meaning of an Italian word he'd happened upon while reading Dante.

What was the reason for this abrupt halt in our exchange of letters? There was a reason, of course, and it was serious. In that last letter John took refuge in a jocular tone, displaying the familiar irony he reserved for those moments life chose him as a target:

> "Caro, Fabio
> Grazie for your letter tanto gentile and circumspect. Sto benissimo, anzi chichissimo with a black patch, just like Dayan prepared to lead the home armies."

He had recently had an operation for the removal of an eye. I believe him, however, when he says he was chichissimo with his black pirate's patch. I don't think I ever met a man more elegant than John, who was elegant on every occasion. It wasn't simply an exterior elegance, either. He possessed an innate refinement which I'm sure didn't make the frequent collisions he had with life any easier.

For this reason, perhaps, he was a man who kept himself hidden. Through writing he found a way to conceal, and yet to reveal, himself at the same time.

He wasn't happy in his suburban Roman work-room, far from

the grand apartment in which he lived. Writing made him suffer. This suffering, it seemed to me, was due to life bestowing on him an excess of material, an abundance that ultimately disturbed him. He sought out the ineffable, dismantling the clumsy mechanism of existence to recompose airy mobiles sustained by the simple strength of his words. Sometimes he made false starts and he'd begin again, obstinate, determined, painstaking.

Our meetings took place in Rome, Sperlonga, London, and Amsterdam. The beauty with which he surrounded himself was a natural or, more precisely, an inevitable part of his life. This was true also of homoeopathy and psychoanalysis, about which he offered advice on the advantages to those of his friends, myself included, whom he thought it might benefit.

Indirectly the influence of psychoanalysis is also evident in John's stories and, especially, in the way he lived as a writer. I think we both suffered from the same disease, if it can be called one, which an analyst has defined as "névrose d'échec". He weaves it into the emotional fabric of his work and it is present in the brusqueness with which he reveals the conflicts that lie at the root of his stories, stories that almost always combine pain with an irrational optimism.

The microscopic doses, the centesimal dilutions of homoeopathy also played a role in John Becker's work, which was in part an attempt to heal the existential malady of the writer, his "male di esistere". For wasn't the endless rewriting, the constant stream of revisions, similar to the whole process of homoeopathic dilution? He administered literature, writing, like minute daily doses of a poison that would allow the sufferer to survive but not guarantee any cure.

It seems to me that every writer, in that moment when he chooses to write, turns his back on life. To dissect life, to transfer it with the immutable perfection of style, to the written page, is a little like using the art of an embalmer. And yet we continue to write because it's the only way we can hope to leave an imprint of our feelings, etch the trail of a thought.

Which is what I myself am attempting to do here, aware of the inadequacy of these words, aware of my inability to bring alive the memory of my friend John Becker in his entirety as a man. John

Becker who, with this small collection of stories, his last statement, published after his death, takes his final and definite leave of this life. But not of me.

Translated by Vida Adamoli

TANYA LITVINOV

John in Chelsea

It was through John Cheever, John's Roman and my Moscow friend, that we met for the first time. Except that there never was a first time, for of course we had met long before I walked into that three-storied Chelsea house late one summer afternoon in 1977. I was startled not to see a little peaked beard to go with the trim little white moustache on the face of the courteous gentleman who opened the door and welcomed me in.

John Becker was not in the least like Uncle Yasha, my father's cousin. But perhaps it was owing to this aberration of mine that I do not seem to remember the time when John and I had been strangers. During all those pleasant teas, lunches, dinners and walks along the Brighton seafront or the lanes in Hampstead we did not tell one another the story of our lives. We did not have to.

Once, John told me, in high glee, that something very funny had happened to him that day; he was eighty.

What made John such a delightful companion was his immense capacity for delight. The small bulging houses of Brighton delighted him, the leafiness of Hampstead, the clutter of the V and A, the Greek sculptures at the British Museum, the Opera, the discovery that I hated Angela Rippon as much as he did.

Hearing him talk of his eye operation would make you think he delighted in that too, with such obvious relish did he dwell on his coming-to and discovering 'two birds' at his bedside feeding him with homoeopathic potions every fifteen minutes – Haidee and Gregory, his daughter and son-in-law.

Most of all he delighted in his little grandson Jacob – was he named after Jaimie of the *After Geneva* stories? In the less than three years they were to have together he seemed to cram all the affection he felt he had been deprived of in his own early days.

The house in Glebe Place was the brightest and warmest I had been inside in my then two-years' experience of London. The walls

9

were hung with beautiful paintings which seemed to glow with the added radiance of being daily enjoyed by their owner. Some of them were by artists hitherto unknown to me, others bore names echoing in all the picture galleries of the world. None had the palling effect of a framed investment one so often experiences in rich men's homes. I was to learn later from John that in his time he had had to give up running a picture gallery in New York because he could not bear to part with the pictures he liked, nor buy those he did not.

That first summer we met de Kooning was showing at the Serpentine, and our souls were united in our delight at the bronze sculptures which he was exhibiting for the first time in England. It turned out John owned a pre-expressionist, beautifully balanced, very early de Kooning. He had bought it, John told me, when the artist was young and needy and 'seemed to be a nice guy'.

His driving passion was to give. Give, give, give – not because he was a do-gooder, not because of the guilty social conscience of the haves (though he confessed to experiencing the occasional twinge), but because of an obsession to fill up the void in the world which he recognized from his own childhood. He gave feasts – prepared by Ah-Lee, his wonderful Chinese cook – to his friends, presents to their grandchildren and – on top of a generous tip – peppermint toffees to cabbies.

One afternoon I found Ah-Lee fuming in the hall, John struggling in the coils of the telephone, maps of London strewn all over the carpet and a beautiful young woman standing uncomfortably in the middle of the room. John had come out to meet me, it appeared, and met this lovely Italian girl instead. In the middle of King's Road, without a word of English, clutching at a piece of paper with the address of an Italian friend who was staying with some English people whose name she did not know, it seemed only natural that in her distress she should have singled out John in the busy summer crowd. And what more natural than for John to bring her home, prepared to supply her with information, encouragement and shelter. The address she had been given merely stated the name of the street without mentioning either the borough or postal index. It took a good half hour and what seemed endless telephone solicitations before John

10

succeeded in unravelling the mystery of London topography. And as he was pressing a glass of wine and a biscuit on her, making sure she had the fare to get there and extracting a promise she would call him up should any hitch occur, the thought crossed my mind that the Cheeryble Brothers were not dead, they had merely become an expatriate American writer in Chelsea.

In me he saw an orphan and a waif, and the fact that I was plus/minus sixty had not blurred his vision. Accordingly, he treated me as a princess. He introduced me to oysters (they did not agree with me), took me to the theatre (I usually dragged him out after the first act) and gave me Karen Blixen's *Out of Africa* to read, a joy forever.

Writing, for John, was another form of giving, the only hard one for him. He was a careful and costive writer. Through the five or six years I had known him he was engaged on a story about a woman running a picture gallery (loosely based on Peggy Guggenheim, he told me) and a flash-in-the-pan artist. He would show it me from time to time. It changed a lot in the process. But all versions had one thing in common: a violent end.

I often wondered, and wonder still, why such a gentle gentleman should have such partiality, a thirst almost, for these catastrophic terminations. Was it fed from the same source as his generosity – the unsated hunger for his parents' love, which took the form of kindness in life and anger in art?

From his own evidence, all through the Jaimie stories, the affection he may have lacked from his parents he got from cousins, nannies, chauffeurs and their disreputable sweethearts. I do not even wholly accept his parents' unlove, convincing as the passionate invective contained in the stories may seem to be. They were probably undemonstrative, wrapped up in their own joys and woes and insensitive to the eternal clamour for more. And Jaimie, the poor little rich boy, was a very Oliver for affection. Perhaps it is those fated to remain Jaimies to the end of their lives who are the ones who become writers.

I am trying to remember when it was that I saw him last. He had a way of slipping out of one's life when things were not so good for him. There never was a last time.

II

Jacob

Jacob looked out into the cold black emptiness. He had been a good builder and his storm-windows held against the sharp sifting snow. But for the first time in his life he didn't care. There was no balm in Gilead, not even pride, only fear.

The storm had begun with Rachel's labour and the storm was still going on, but upstairs with the women there was sudden quiet, and in his heart Jacob knew. Only there is the word at the end as well as at the beginning and, with his head against the cold pane, Jacob waited for it.

Overhead the door opened and closed. Sophia came down the stairs and stood by Jacob at the window. She had been Jacob's housekeeper before Rachel came and she was a true daughter of Job, for she was to bury her parents and, after them, one by one, their great lonely brood; Sophia, the real woman of sorrow because there was never to be a sorrow all her own. This was the first scene in her long play.

"The child, Uncle Jake ...."
"Sag es mir nicht."
"The child will live. But Rachel ...." Sophia broke.

Jacob's heart broke too, but he gave no sign. His great love went hot and sick inside him and gushed up at his throat, but it ran deep and found no outlet. There was the sound of Sophia's sobbing and then, against it, the infant cry from above the stairs.

Jacob had waited so long for Rachel. Not that he hadn't a way with the girls. Even as a boy back in Bingen, on that terrible day at the bridge when the *verdammte Catholische* had called him a dirty *Jude* and stoned him, one of their daughters was waiting on a side road. That was perhaps what made his love so provocative – the terrible coat of revenge. At twenty, after the long voyage was over,

15

he was already the fine figure of a man when Mrs. Hellman (even Mrs Hellman, the wife of the New York banker!) gave him a gold watch to tick – rich, close and hidden in his natty vest – as he peddled his way across the new world. Not that Jacob had been forward with a great Jewish lady like Mrs. Hellman, but, always the gallant, his nostrils had sensed the sachet at the black-laced breasts and that had been adulation enough for Mrs. Hellman. Anyhow it got him the watch, and he had a way with the farmers' wives too coming across Pennsylvania and Ohio and Indiana, and when he reached Jackson his wagon had already been twice restocked.

He was a strong man and a gay man, a hard trader and proud of it. He had the thriftiness that some wanderers acquire. In New England it is called yankee and for his people it is called shrewdness. Perhaps there is a difference in kind. In any event Jacob's shrewdness was healthy because it was directed by a strong sense of duty and tempered, now and then, with kindness. The more his success became assured, the more he repeated that "honesty was the best policy", and he repeated this so often that in the end he came not only to believe it but to practice it. His store shingle read "Jake Loeb, All-Wool Clothier", and he was known and pleased to be known as "the only honest Jew in Jackson". This questionable compliment was no great distinction, for there were then few Jews in Jackson and most of the few were Jacob's relatives, imported by Jacob, and, besides, it was fantasy, because as Jacob also knew, there is no more all-anything in the clothes men wear than in the men who wear them. Jacob was simply a good advertiser and, in this sense, being a man of vision, it is more than likely that he helped to circulate the saying himself. As a result of it – and his fair trading – the farmers came in to buy from as far as Niles. With the extra pair of pants he always had an off-color story for the boys and, when it was really a bad one, his eyes would cry in appreciation of the telling. His eyes were outside in the wagons too, for he was not unmindful that it had been ladies first with his success as well as with his pleasure, and so everyone was pleased. But if not circumspect, he was careful for after all he was a citizen now and a respected one; he blew the schofar in the little

16

synagogue and there had been talk of running him for mayor.

But still he didn't marry. The Widow Jessup, with the best lands around Vandercook's had, as everyone knew, set her cap for him, and Jacob, ever the gallant, played the game, but he never took it seriously because it never crossed his mind that he might marry a gentile. As his sisters married, he dutifully feathered their nests, and then they in turn did some importing, "match-making" as it was laughingly called and seriously meant. But although both Rosa Nathan and Johanna Stiefel were daughters of old family friends, of good German-Jewish stock, presentable and properly trained, even waiting for little more than to be efficient *hausfraus*, they didn't make the grade. There was something lacking, elegance or some remembrance of Mrs. Hellman or perhaps even poetry, something in any case that Jacob didn't have. Yet he was lonesome.

In 1880 Jacob had been in Jackson twenty years. He made only two annual trips now, trading a little in corn and keeping his hand in with the farmers, goodwill tours on the side but their purpose was his business, wool.

The rains came late that year. Jacob waited for them and then drove southeast through the Irish Hills. As the road unwound, Jacob was at home with it, for he knew almost every tree along the ways of southern Michigan. And how he loved Michigan! The state was not so old then and people still parented it, watching full of pride. To Jacob it was something even more, for it is only the oppressed of course who can evaluate liberty. Driving in the evening through the green land Jacob's heart was grateful and happy, as if a burden had been forever lifted. He was free and secure, and he was also a man alone on a trip to whom any adventure might befall. Still, he was a lonely man, not yet tired, for there was still lots to be done, but a little empty.

He drove southeast, through Napolean, and crossed into Indiana. It always seemed to him remarkable how suddenly inferior the border states became. Even the rains in Indiana were

17

unpredictable. They started again and, when he drove into Ike Och's place, he was wet through, angry and laughing at the same time.

With schnapps and dry clothes it was warm and friendly at Ike's. Ike was a fine fellow even though he would never get anywhere, for he was too much the gentleman with a fondness for fancy things, good tobacco, fine schnapps, flowers in flowered vases; bad luck, perhaps for he had lost his wife, Miriam.

Ike's daughter, Rachel, served them. She had been a little girl two springs ago. Now, suddenly, perhaps on that evening in response to Jacob's presence, she was a woman, tall and fine, proud and gentle, too, carefully looking at no one as she served her father and his guest, silently sitting between them. She had the fine hands of a princess – she was a princess from another world. Jacob looked at his own hairy hands with the hard pink palms. The girl looked too.

The next day the rains were gone but Jacob stayed on and courted Rachel. He worshipped her; his hard body needed her, and yet, as she responded, she made him gentle. She was not twenty and he was twice as old. Still it was a good match for Rachel, indeed, better than she knew; beauty and the wonderful beast, the strong father and the great lover all in one.

They were married in December. Jacob drove his bride up through the Michigan snow. Her sealskin turban and fine gold earrings set off the flushed, smooth skin as they came down Main. For years afterwards it was said that she had been the most beautiful woman in southern Michigan.

All was in readiness for the princess-bride. Under Jacob's direction, the house on First had been made over, spotless; there was even a little dressing alcove near the great marriage bed and, extravagence of extravagences, a hired girl was waiting. The great ladies of Jackson came to welcome Rachel; they were curious about these foreigners and yet they recognized the strange breeding, and

18

they all knew love when they saw it, some for the having and more for the wanting. All the world loves a lover and Jacob could have been mayor that year for the asking, President if the people of Jackson could have done the choosing. But Jacob's course was fixed, his lucky star shone in its proper orbit – the rise with Venus, the morning trip to the store, and back at night to his heart's desire.

Rachel was everything that could be wished for: beautiful and industrious, polite and a little distant with the relatives, courteous and a little shy with the callers, of straight carriage in company, bending and close only for Jacob. She was with child that spring and then in January the idyll was over; Rachel bore her Lord the child and died.

Jaimie

Jaimie liked to sit next to Schultz better than anything; of course better than being with Bessie because, well, he was too old for Bessie now; better than with Phelps and the other boys although he liked them too but they didn't know and Schultz did; better than with his father although his father was such a fine lawyer that he was elected to the board of the National Bank of the Republic and a good golfer and popular both with men and women; and better than with his mother, who was lovely and so refined that she knew not only about gardens but had studied Chinese art a little too and was on civic committees like garbage disposal and was charming and a best bridge player and dressed beautifully always. Because of all these things Jaimie couldn't at first understand why he wanted to be with Schultz so much. He knew it was wrong because his mother and father didn't like it and he felt bad about it but he just couldn't help it.

Schultz told Jaimie that he shouldn't be telling him these things, that Jaimie's father should and that if he had a boy like Jaimie he'd want to talk to him.

Jaimie said he guessed his father didn't have the time with the office and board meetings and things like that.

Schultz said his brother ran two barber shops and sometimes wasn't home until midnight and still had time to talk to Schultz's nephew – and he didn't have a wonderful chauffeur to drive him around either. Jaimie laughed. Schultz said his brother had told his nephew everything.

"Everything!?"

"Yes, everything." Schultz's nephew was thirteen and knew everything.

Ha, ha. Jaimie was only twelve and knew almost everything.

Schultz was twenty-eight, hairy, dark, stocky with full lips. Had he been a boxer his nose would have been punched in.

Before he became a chauffeur, he had been a taxi driver. Chicago was wide open in those days, the red light district with houses along South State. Some of them gave free shows downstairs, not just stripteases always either like now.

"Whatdyamean?"

Well, Schultz had seen a girl once, after she'd stripped, say, "Who wants me? If you're a man, come up and take me. It's for free."

"Did anyone go?"

"Sure."

"Who?"

"Oh, a big bozo ... like a yokel or a miner."

"Why did she do it?"

"To get business. It excited the men and then afterwards they'd go upstairs."

"Did you go?"

"No, I didn't have to get mine that way."

When Schutlz was twenty-one he drove his cab nights. He used to call for a woman at one of the houses. She was a madame. She lived in the old Dakota Hotel.

She always tipped him nice. Then once, after she'd paid him, she said, "You're a good-looking boy. Why don't you come up and see me?"

So he parked his cab and went up. She told him "If you want to be good, you've got to know how." She knew too. He used to go and see her regular after that. She was very clean. She taught him everything.

"What?"

"Oh," Schultz laughed, "that would be telling."

Schultz said he could control every muscle he had. He said that he'd worked out in a gym, that it took a long time but he could control every muscle in his body.

"*Every* muscle?"

"Yes, *every* muscle."

21

Jaimie sat with Schultz all the time, outside the house, while his mother was shopping, waiting at his father's office, riding downtown and back or to the club in the country.

His father said that he was with Schultz too much. He asked what they talked about.

"Oh, I don't know."

"Well, what?"

"Oh, nothing, everything."

Then one time, coming back from the country when Jaimie started to get in next to Schultz, his father said, "No, you come back and sit with us."

"Why?"

"Just come back."

Jaimie said nothing all the way in. It got dark outside, like the end of the world.

When they got home his father said he didn't like Jaimie's being with Schultz all the time and if it didn't stop he'd have to let Schultz go, that from then on Jaimie was to sit in the back of the car.

"Even when I'm alone with him!?"

Jaimie was so upset that his mother made his father change it: he was to sit in the back when his mother had no one else with her. That was bad enough.

Schultz was very polite to Jamie's parents. When his father talked to Schultz through the car tube, Schultz's face never changed at all. It was funny, a man like Schultz acting, well, like a dog when he got orders. With Jaimie's mother it was not quite the same because Schultz always smiled or turned back to ask about an address.

Schultz liked Jaimie's mother because when the new car came, a Hudson landau, his mother had the front changed because she said she didn't have the heart to have a man outside in the awful Chicago weather. The car wasn't quite so elegant with the change but it was still pretty snazzy. Jaimie had never thought of his mother being like the car until once, in the late afternoon, when he and Schultz were waiting outside the dressmaker's, his mother came out in a new coat. She must have been going some place special because otherwise she never wore her sapphire necklace in the daytime. Jaimie knew that the necklace was elegant because everybody talked about it; it didn't have just blue sapphires but all colors and they were fastened together with little diamonds which, in the light, sparkled. When she came out, Schultz did a low whistle and whispered, "Elegant." Jaimie was surprised. Of course he knew that his mother was lovely. His father said so often enough and sometimes other people besides, and when he had new boyfriends at the house, afterwards they'd say, "You've a nice mother. Good-looking too."

Schultz said that women were always going into the Greek shoe-makers on 47th Street. He had a curtain in the back of his shop and a little room behind it with a shoe stand.

"A shoe stand!"

"Yep. He locks the door and then later, from the little room, he lets them out in the alley."

"Why a shoe stand?"

"Lots of women like what he does better."

"What?"

Schultz slowly licked his lips.

Jaimie's mother said it was because Bessie was Irish that she was so gifted at potato peeling. She used a very sharp knife, peeled them paper thin and, when she set her mind to it, she could peel without breaking a paring. By putting eyes in them, when Jaimie was little, she used to make snakes.

"You're getting too big for the pantry now," said Bessie, who had asked him in. "Maybe that's why you like to be with Schultz so much."

Bessie was jealous!

"How come you're everybody's favourite, Jaimie?"

"Am I?"

She brought him the frosting bowl. The chocolate was not quite hard, just the way he liked it. He was her favourite, that was for sure.

On Monday nights Jaimie's father and mother had season tickets for the opera and his mother had a season ticket for the symphony on Friday afternoons. She said the real music lovers went on Saturday nights but Friday was more convenient besides being a kind of ladies' day for the nicest women in Chicago. Monday was the most fashionable night for the opera too.

On Mondays Jaimie's father and mother usually had dinner earlier and then got dressed up; Bessie wouldn't have time to eat because she had to hurry upstairs to help. After they'd gone, she'd gobble her dinner and then rush back up to Jaimie. She could be with him on other nights too, but Monday was special because of their coming home so late on account of the opera. Even so it was scary reading the sex books that Bessie had found on the shelf in the closet.

Her favorite was *The Blindness of Virtue.* It was a play about a man who was engaged to a girl and went to visit in her house. One night her parents were called away and she became frightened or cold or lonesome or something and came in his room and got in bed with him. He jumped up and ran around the room hitting the furniture and grinding his teeth and pulling his hair and saying things like, "O God, I can't stand it," "Lord help me why am I such a beast" and "Please, God, pity her." Bessie always read it aloud and got excited and red in the face but Jaimie thought it was funny.

When Jaimie told Schultz about it he said Jaimie knew too much for that kind of kid stuff.

Schultz let Jaimie steer, at first in the country and then in the city. Jaimie would sit real close with Schultz's gloved hands around him. If anything came along, Schultz would grab the wheel.

"Why did you wait so long?"

"Don't worry. I'm here."

Later he almost never grabbed the wheel no matter what happened.

'Why?"

"You've got to learn your own control."

Still he was there.

24

That winter they went to Coronado Beach. Jaimie and his mother took the train, Schultz drove the car out and his father came for Christmas. Jaimie wanted to drive out with Schultz but he wasn't allowed to.

At Coronado Beach there was a long esplanade with very few cars, so Schultz really taught Jaimie to drive. It wasn't very hard as Jaimie was already a good steerer. At first he sat between Schultz's legs. The only difficult part was the gas and spark lever but Schultz said they weren't important, the important thing was the brake: you've always got to have her under control, even if it's slippery and wet and then you shouldn't use the brake at all! When it rained he showed Jaimie by skidding all over the place and around to a dead stop by the water.

When Jaimie's father came out they drove down the esplanade to show him. When they reached a safe place, Schultz as usual got out to open the door, but when his father got in front beside Jaimie, Schultz didn't get back in but shut both doors. He said, "I'll wait here."

That was the only time Jaimie's father wanted Schultz next to Jaimie because he jumped out and put Schultz back in front. Jaimie drove down the esplanade, turned around and back to the starting place. But Schultz said, "Drive your father back to the hotel."

So Jaimie did. His father, who couldn't drive, was so impressed that Jaimie didn't care if he sat in front with Schultz or not .... for a while, anyway.

That summer Jaimie's parents rented a big house in Winnetka. It was so big that besides Bessie and the cook they had to have a second maid.

Her name was Rosa. She wore glasses and came from Luxemburg and didn't smile even when she arranged the flowers.

Schultz said she was after him, that she kept bothering him and that she'd better leave him alone.

"Why?"

'She better had, that's all." Schultz was very angry. His face hardened and the sides almost twitched.

'Why, what would you do?''

"I'd give it to her until she'd wish she'd never seen me, that's what I'd do."

Schultz lived with a woman who worked nights mostly.
"Oh."
Yes, but not before fixing him up. She cooked for him wonderful and that wasn't all. He didn't run around, he didn't have to: what he got was so good.
"Is she nice?"
"Mm,hm."
"Like my mother?"
"Sweeter."
Is she as pretty?"
"Well, she hasn't got pearls to show herself off in." Schultz laughed. "what she's got's better."
"Diamonds?"
"Yes."
"Did you give them to her?"
"God did. Here and here," and Schultz touched his chest and crotch. "I just keep 'em polished."
Schultz lived in a big block of flats on the West Side. Sometimes he drove Jaimie by but he'd never take him up.
He said there was a tall woman across the hall, red haired, a good-looker. She would come out with her negligée half open and it wasn't hard to see what she was after. But Schultz never went in.
"Why?"
"Never shit on your own doorstep, Jaimie."

Once Jaimie said, "Why don't you take me with you?"
"Where?"
"To watch."
Schultz was surprised and shocked and pleased too. He maybe thought he had a good pupil. Maybe he was tempted too because it took him a long time to say, "No."
"Why?"
"I couldn't."

26

Maybe he didn't dare. Jaimie kept on pestering him and he always laughed as if he liked the idea until once he said, "What's the good in watching? The fun's in doing it, but what's your hurry? You'll do it fine. Half of it's making them want it, you know, and they'll want it from you."

"Why will they?"

"I see the girls look at you. They're not just looking at me up here."

Jaimie laughed but he didn't really believe that they were looking at him when they could see Schultz sitting there.

Maybe Schultz would have taken him anyway but then one morning he wasn't there.

Jaimie's father telephoned his flat but there was no answer. Then he telephoned the garage and they said the car hadn't been there all night. Yes, they were sure.

Jaimie's father was so excited that he woke up his mother. The worst part was that she got dressed and took Jaimie to school in a taxi. On the way Jaimie was so despondent that his mother said he didn't have to stay for woodcraft and could come home early. She promised to telephone him if she found out anything special.

When he came home his mother said there had been an accident. "No, not serious ... he hurt his toe."

"His toe! Where is he?"

"In the hospital."

Jaimie wanted to go right away but his mother didn't know which hospital. His mother was not a good liar because when she did her eyes opened very wide. She didn't give a decent answer to any question and then she said what she always said when she didn't know what to say: "Wait until your father comes home."

But his father didn't tell him anything either. They both knew too. Bessie said they did. She brought him his supper like always when he didn't go downstairs and then sat and spoon-fed him the way she did when he was small. He didn't care enough to turn his head away to make her coax him.

She said she'd listened while they talked on the phone. It was about Schultz's woman, who'd been in trouble before. She had a police record.

"Did you know he lived with a woman, Jaimie?"

"Yes I did."

"They found the car in Detroit. So it looks like they've gone over into Canada. Your mother's tortoise case with the cards and dollar bills was still there. So he wasn't a thief anyway. Maybe he murdered somebody though. But even if he did, he'll be coming back to see you anyway."

"Why will he?"

"Because you're his friend. Whenever he came into the kitchen for a snack and coffee, he'd always say, 'Hurry, please, my friend Jaimie's out there and I can't keep my best friend waiting'."

Tears trickled out.

"Your father was real nice, though. He told the police that now they'd found the car and it wasn't damaged, he was no longer interested, they didn't have to look for him.

"Oh."

"So it isn't that terrible, is it, Jaimie-boy?"

"Yes, it is, Bessie."

He turned his head away. He could understand Schultz's having taken the car, as awful as it was, but not without telling him first. Why, after all their secret talks?

Bessie took the tray and closed the door. Then, as usual, she stood outside listening. She wouldn't hear him crying though, because he'd stuffed his head in the pillow.

Jaimie told his mother that after school he was going over to Phelps Malloy's. His mother kissed him. She was happy because when Schultz was there his mother and father were always asking why he didn't go over and play with the other boys.

He took the number 4 streetcar. He sat quiet but he was not quiet inside. He didn't think Schultz was back but he wanted to see.

He didn't know the name of the street but he found the block of flats. There were so many of them he didn't know which exactly. One of them was marked JANITOR but nobody answered.

It began to rain and so he ran up and down the stairways. They were all dark and only a few of them were clean. He guessed

28

Schultz would have lived in a clean one. All of them, though, had writing on the walls.

A tall woman with reddish hair came down the stairs. But not in a negligée.

"Excuse me. Do you know someone named Schultz?"

"Who?"

"The man who lives across the hall."

"No one lives across from me, sonny."

She put her umbrella up and went out.

He had to wait a long time for a number 4 and got wet through. Riding in it was like the time in the car, cold and dark outside like the end of the world, only this time it was the end for sure.

When he got home his mother said, "Jaimie!" Where have you been?"

He sneezed.

"Get those clothes off."

She came upstairs with him and ran the bath.

"Why didn't you call up? The car's back. We have another driver."

"What's he like?"

"He seems all right. He's not like Schultz, though."

He believed her.

Jaimie had caught cold. His legs ached, he had a pain on his left side and a little temperature.

The cold went away but the aches and pains stayed on and so did the temperature. Dr. Abt came, joked, tapped and listened. He said Jaimie had a touch of rheumatic fever, that it wasn't anything serious but it seemed to have affected his heart, just a little bit. He was supposed to stay in bed and rest.

"For how long?"

Well, Dr. Abt didn't know.

Afterwards there was the usual hushhush in the den with Jaimie's mother. Then Dr. Abt came back, sat on the bed and asked if Jaimie had any questions.

"Will I die?"

"I hope so – in a hundred years or maybe less. But your mother will if you worry her. Be a good boy and stay quiet."

Then he moved closer and took Jaimie's hand in his tough fat one.

"Does anything bother you lately, Jaimie?"

"Did my mother tell you to ask me?"

"Would it be so terrible if she had?"

Jaimie thought it over. "No, because there isn't anything."

Jaimie's mother had beautiful hands that felt cool and lovely on his forehead. She didn't keep them there long because she always thought he felt hot and would get up to take his temperature. She was wonderful at straightening the pillows and making everything fresh. She said that when she was a girl she wanted to be a trained nurse but that her father wouldn't let her.

After breakfast in bed she'd always come in and stay with Jaimie, although she would leave to give orders for the house and of course she always had to go into her room to answer the telephone. She had many lady friends and her favorite, Alma Fellows, was almost lovelier than she. She would tell Jaimie what Alma and the others said, but she said they weren't as truthful as she was. She said she was an exceptionally truthful person. She thought a lie was an awful thing, not a white lie maybe which one said only on special occasions so as not to hurt someone's feelings.

"Like what?"

"Oh, if someone isn't looking well or has bought a hideous hat."

She thought this was funny and laughed and so did Jaimie.

She said that she and Jaimie must always be truthful with one another and that it would be awful if Jaimie didn't tell her everything.

Jaimie giggled.

His mother asked why but she couldn't help laughing too. Then, as if she knew what he was thinking, she asked, "Do you miss Schultz?"

"Yes, some."

That same afternoon Phelps came over.

"Where'd you go that afternoon when you got sick?"

30

"Why?"

"Your mother thought you were at our place."

"How do you know?"

"She called up."

So she knew, or something anyway, and that was why she talked about lying. But was she lying too by pretending not to know? And why was he supposed to tell everything when all he ever heard was from Bessie and they didn't tell him anything that he really wanted to know?

The aches and pains got better but being in bed every day got worse. There was nothing worth anything with Schultz gone. The only man Jaimie saw was his father. He'd come home in the late afternoons, say hello and go lie down in the den. He could drop right off to sleep and in just a few minutes wake up refreshed. After dinner, when he didn't go out, he'd come and sit with Jaimie for a while. He'd tell about all the important matters he'd had to deal with, the advice he'd given and how he'd reorganized this and that. He didn't just reorganize in Chicago, he went to New York and Pittsburg and other places. For a little man, Jaimie's mother said, he was a wonder at reorganizing big companies.

Dr. Abt said Jaimie could start getting up. Gradually, at first only a few minutes, then more and more.

Jaimie's mother was so happy that she couldn't wait to tell his father if he called from Pittsburg. She kissed him and said, "Hearts of palm, alligator pear, French lamb chops and sherbert, I can't stand it anymore" and went off to her Thursday luncheon.

Bessie took her sweet time coming up with the tray. Then, when she came in, she was smiling funny.

"What's the matter with you?"

She took a letter from her apron. It was for his father.

"Look on the back."

Hermann Schultz 59 Winder St. Detroit Mich

"I'll bet you'd like to know what's in it."

Jaimie looked at her.

31

"I know."

"How?"

"Cross your heart."

Jaimie did.

"I steamed it open ... because I knew you'd want to know. Look how neat I glued it back."

"Why didn't you let me see it?"

"He didn't say much except that he has three weeks' pay coming and some vacation money. I say he should have thought of that before he took the car. The part about the vacation money is true, though; remember..."

"What else did he say?"

"He said he did it because his fiancée – he calls her his fiancée – was in trouble and they need a lawyer bad. He said he was desperate and could your father lend him five hundred dollars. He said he knew he'd done wrong but the car wasn't scratched and he'd worked honest for over two years."

"Did he say anything about me?"

"No, nor me neither." Bessie laughed.

"Take the tray."

"You didn't touch it."

"Please, Bessie."

She knew when not to argue.

500 dollars! Jaimie had 117 in the marble bag saved for everything: for the trip with Phelps to Starved Rock, for *The Negro Children's Fresh Air* and maybe for a dog next summer. Would his father give it, or would he if Jaimie gave his 117? With Schultz so desperate Jaimie couldn't stand it any longer if they didn't tell him anything.

It was a surprise all right. What happened was that Bessie came in and said two men were bringing a crate upstairs. Of course when he saw it he knew right away what was in it because he'd wanted one for so long.

It was complete with records and with a card that said,

To while away the weary hours love Dad

He handled it like it might break. He played *When Irish Eyes are*

32

Smiling for Bessie and because his mother asked to hear Geraldine Farrer he played *Butterfly* for her. The vic had a beautiful deep clear tone. Then he closed it and locked it.

"What are you doing that for?"

"I think Dad should take it back."

"Why?"

"He didn't know I was getting up when he sent it."

"That's the silliest thing I ever heard of."

"I'll wait and see what he thinks anyway."

"You mean you're not going to play it until Sunday!" His mother was getting mad.

"I didn't have it while I was sick, so what'll a couple more days hurt?"

His mother got up and walked out. Later she sent Bessie in to see what she could do.

"Your mother's real upset that you're so pig-headed. I must say that with the beautiful machine I don't understand it either." It was funny that she didn't.

Would his father send the 500? Or would he if Jaimie returned the vic and gave the money-bag-money? 500 − 117 = 373. But even with the records it didn't cost that much. Worse still: if he wasn't supposed to know what was in his father's letter, how could he talk about it?

There was one chance:

"There's a letter from Schultz in the den."

"For me?"

"No, for father."

"How do you know about it?"

"I saw it. Could you read it to me? Please."

"Open someone else's mail? I wouldn't dream of such a thing."

So that was that. Maybe he'd have to tell on Bessie. He couldn't say he steamed the letter open himself because then his father might be so angry that he wouldn't send anything at all. Jaimie thought and figured and worried about it all the time. And then, like Aladdin's lamp, out of the blue, the answer came! Schultz had written him too. Jaimie wished he really had. He pretended that he had:

Dear Jaimie,

How are you? I miss you very much.

Then just exactly like the letter to his father but with a different end:

Much love Schultz.

Well, maybe not "much", maybe not even "love". Maybe just "your best friend Schultz."

Jaimie's mother could usually get his father to do what she wanted. Once, though, when she had asked something in front of Alma Fellows, his father had said "No" and when he left the room Alma laughed her lovely tinkly laugh and said, "Edith, you're so naive. If you really want something from Edgar, ask it lying down."

Jaimie of course knew what Alma meant but he thought it might be better if he talked with his father lying down anyway. So he did his time up early Sunday morning and was back in bed when his father came home. His father came up to see him straight away; he was glad that Jaimie was better but he was so excited about the wonderful reorganization he'd made in Pittsburg that he couldn't wait to tell Jaimie's mother about it. First, though, he asked Jaimie how he liked the victrola but he didn't stay to hear.

His father had to tell his partner too about the wonderful reorganization and so he went out and came back late for Sunday dinner and with one thing and another he didn't come in to sit with Jaimie until Sunday afternoon.

"Well, now. Your mother tells me you've been waiting for me. You didn't have to do that, Jaimie. Let's play it."

But Jaimie didn't.

"What's the matter?"

"How much did it cost?"

"That's a strange question. Why?"

"Wouldn't it be better maybe to give the money to somebody poor?"

"We give generously enough to the poor."

"I don't mean like that. I mean somebody we know."

34

"Who?"

Jaimie looked down. "Schultz." When he looked up his father was staring at him.

"Did you open my letter?"

"He wrote me too."

"I'd like to see it."

"All he said was that he was sorry he took the car but his girl was in trouble and he needed five hundred dollars. Will you send it to him?"

Because Jamie's father was still staring at him Jamie felt he had to say more. "He said he was writing me because I was his friend and maybe I should speak with you about it."

"I see."

"Will you send it?"

"No."

"Why?"

"As a reward for stealing or to help him get mixed up with a woman of that kind?"

"How do you know what she's like?"

"She has a police record. Of course, strictly speaking that's not my concern. But what is my concern and inexcusable is for a man to involve a thirteen year old boy in his private affairs. Because of your loyalty I might have sent him something in addition to his claim, but certainly not now, for what he's done is unpardonable."

"Oh." Then very low Jamie said, "He didn't write to me."

"Then you read my letter after all?"

"Yes."

His father stood up. Jaimie thought he was going to hit him. He did worse. "You know what Schultz thinks I owe him. Well, I know of no law that states that one is obliged to pay a thief. In view of what you've done and so that you will think twice before doing such a thing again, I shall send nothing."

Jaimie lay there. Maybe he should have said how Bessie opened the letter. Maybe for Schultz's sake he should have. But even for Schultz he just couldn't tell on poor Bessie. It was her night off so his mother brought up the tray. She said his father was very upset and that Jaimie should apologize. But his father didn't come in again.

Jaimie took down the marble bag. There was 90 in bills and 27 in change. He stuffed in handkerchiefs so that coins couldn't rattle and put the bag in his mackintosh. It would look funny travelling without a suitcase and so he took his schoolbag. He put in the cold meat from the tray and sweater and scarf to stuff it out with.

Downstairs everything was like always before he'd been sick: the umbrella stand, the front parlour, the dent in the wall near the washroom. He opened the vestibule door and closed it until he heard the click. Then he put his shoes on. It was cold and so he tied the scarf around his head. He wasn't shaky at all.

In the streetcar it wasn't like the time he'd gone to Schultz's flat because then he knew he shouldn't have gone. This time he had to go; because Schultz wasn't getting any money at all just on account of something Jaimie had done; why, Schultz didn't even know about it! Jaimie hoped that the 117 less the train fare would be as much as the salary anyway.

It was still dark in Detroit. Although the money was for Schultz Jaimie took a taxi because he felt wobbly and besides it would have been dangerous scrounging around a strange city with so much money.

59 Winder St. had a vacancy sign in the window. Even so Jaimie had to ring twice before a woman came to the door. She said, "Oh, number 14 on the top floor." As Jaimie started up a bell rang.

Climbing the stairs Jaimie had to rest twice and when he got to the top he was all in. Schultz, bare-chested and bare-footed, was coming out of a room rubbing his eyes like he just woke up. He looked awful: he hadn't shaved and his eyes were puffed. He was so surprised to see Jaimie that he didn't smile. Then he said, "Jaimie , you're so white."

"I've been sick. Can I sit down?"

"Sit here." Schultz pulled down a seat attached to the wall under a telephone. Jaimie thought of their old talks about Schultz's girl and guessed that maybe if he was dying Schultz wouldn't invite him in.

"Why'd you come?"

"Here." Jaimie took out the bag. "It's a hundred and

seventeen dollars less ... well, it's more than a hundred anyway. My father won't send anything."

"Where'd you get this?"

"It's mine. Can I have some water?"

Schultz took the bag and went back in the room. A woman's voice said, "Who?" and then excitedly, "What?!" There was a lot of talking and walking around. Then the door opened and the woman said, "Don't take it there, bring him here" and Schultz came out, this time with his shoes on. He helped Jaimie up and steered him towards the room.

When they got to the door the woman was there. She was in a blue wrapper with a slip underneath that was tight across her big breasts. She was very blond and although not so young very pretty with a wonderful white skin that was powdered and smelled lovely even before Jaimie got in the room.

"Hello, honey," she said, and then to Schultz, "Why don't you help him, you big lummox?" and she came out and put her arms under Jaimie's. "I didn't know you were such a big fellow ... and so good-looking too. You must be dog tired, all that way with all that money."

They were in the room and her perfume was stronger, some kind of Arabian flowers maybe with lilies of the valley.

"Aren't you the wonder boy! A friend in need is a friend indeed. I could kiss you for it. I think I will."

She did everything at once, very quick, talking all the time: helped him down, gave him water, closed the window, opened his tie, put him back on the pillow. As she bent down, he could see in the cleft between her great breasts where Schultz had said the diamonds were and her perfume was so sweet and strong he forgot everything else.

"You're not going to faint, are you?"

He shook his head.

"Well, don't. Anna'll take care of you. I should after all you've done for us. You've saved us. You're our little gentleman saviour. But wait, I'll get something better than water."

There was a wash basin and next to it a gas burner on the bureau. She filled a kettle and put it on. "Is there a drop of rum?" and when Schultz showed her the empty bottle, she said, "Go down and get some ... Old Jamaica ...we can afford it for him."

It was the first time Jaimie had ever been glad to see Schultz leave. It was so funny that he couldn't help smiling: because he had always wanted to come to their flat in Chicago and Schultz wouldn't take him and here in Detroit right off he was in their bed!

Anna took his shoes off, loosened his belt, pulled his trousers off, covered him. She put her hand on his forehead, like his mother but different, not so cool and soothing, but better as if her hand was there to stay. No one had ever touched him like that before.

"My, you're pale. Are you all right?"

He nodded and Schultz came back. Anna took a piece of cake from the box by the window, poured the tea – two cups full – put rum in it and then sat on the bed and spooned it to him. He didn't like it alone but with the crumbly old cake it was just wonderful.

He could hear Schultz blowing and sipping but he couldn't see him. Then Schultz stopped and asked, "Did anyone know you were going away?"

Jaimie shook his head.

"They'll know you've gone though, won't they?"

"What time is it?"

"Nine."

"Maybe."

Anna went on spooning the tea. It was hard to keep his eyes open. As they went shut he saw the white of her lovely skin.

"They'll know you're here, won't they?".

"I guess so."

"I don't like it that they haven't phoned."

"Why?" Anna asked. "Here, honey, finish it and then you can sleep."

"Because I know Jaimie's dad and he won't fool around. If he doesn't find this number he'll call the police."

"Oh!" Anna said and stopped spooning the tea. Jaimie opened his eyes. "Maybe you ought to call him, Hermann."

"Why?" Jaimie asked. "Can't I stay with you a little first? Please."

"Maybe Hermann can tell him you're tuckered out and should rest up with us for a while. We want you, honey. But go on, Hermann, before it's too late."

38

Jaimie was going to say something but Anna kissed him again. "Take it easy," Schultz said, "He's just thirteen and we've had enough trouble." Then he went out.

"You don't like the police much," Jaimie said when the door closed.

"They don't like me, honey."

"Why?"

"I got into trouble, like Hermann said."

"How?"

"I did something wrong."

Jaimie smiled. "It couldn't have been so bad."

"Why?" She smiled back.

"Because you're so nice."

She kissed him again. "It wasn't so nice to pinch your daddy's car. Still and all, bygones are bygones, and it couldn't be helped. What's bad about it is that now we need help with the law and after what's happened we can't turn to your dad. Hermann says he's such a wonderful lawyer he could get anybody out of anything. Do you believe that? Hermann said he's not so hot at home though and no good with you at all. Why? What does he do to you, honey?"

"Nothing. I don't see him much."

"Maybe you're lucky. They're all alike, rich or poor. You should have seen mine ... what a stinker. He never gave me nothing decent. Come to think of it, you're the only man who ever gave me money for nothing and that's the truth. I'll never forget it. Never."

He heard it far off and smiled. He didn't want her to forget.....

"Wake up, honey. I'm sorry you're so sleepy but you can sleep later. You gotta get up now. Look, here's a bacon and egg sandwich all hot and milk. Eat it, honey, and then you gotta go back with Hermann."

"Why do I?"

"Because that's what your daddy said."

"When?"

"An hour or so ago." It was Schultz behind her in the corner. She was dressed now in green, with green lace at her breasts and on her sleeves. She still smelled wonderful.

"Your father said you'd been real sick and that your mother's worried about draughts and everything and that you might get heart trouble again ... So I rented a car with a heater. A Macfarland, Jaimie, the kind you always wanted. It's down in front. You can help me drive her back."

"Are you going?"

She shook her head.

"Then I won't go."

"It's not such a bad idea at that," Schultz said. "We don't have to stay overnight, so who'll know ... except Jaimie's folks. And if you take care of Jaimie on the way, his father might want to thank you, Anna. Yes, I think his folks would appreciate it."

"Oh, I'd do it just for him."

"Then will you go?" Jaimie asked.

"Yes, for you."

"I'll go for you, too."

Jaimie slept all the way to South Chicago. When he woke up his head was in Anna's lap with the flaps of her fur coat around him and she'd covered his feet with a blanket. She'd been dozing too and when he moved she opened her eyes and smiled. She had a red and green handkerchief around her head and with the fur at her neck she looked prettier than ever. As Jaimie sat up he kissed her on the cheek.

"Hey, hey." Schultz said. He must have seen them in the mirror.

Jaimie had to get out and when Schultz pulled up he saw the sky. As he stood in the back of the car he could see the fires from the mills in a great line along the lake. With the red sky in the cold air they were like suns or volcanoes maybe with the fires coming from inside the earth. It was strange and so beautiful, so different from what he had known of Chicago that it was hard to believe that the mills at night were really part of it, just as it was hard to believe that a person like Anna was part of a world so near and yet a world that he had never known.

When he got back in the car, Schultz said, "Aren't you going to spell me? You're a fine pal; you don't help me drive and you take my girl." Then he drove off and the red faded outside and it was black again broken every once in a while by the first city lights.

Jaimie said nothing. He was dreaming how he'd like to go over the whole world with Schultz driving and Anna so warm next to him seeing mills at night and other wonders that he didn't know.

"What are you thinking honey?"

"About the mills ... how beautiful they made everything far away."

"They don't make things so beautiful near up," Anna said. "I know."

The lights were all on in the house. Schultz got out but Anna sat there and so did Jaimie.

"Are you scared of your folks?"

Jaimie shook his head. "I just wanted to stay with you a little more." Then he got out but Anna didn't.

"Aren't you coming?" Schultz asked.

"I don't know," she said, so Jaimie decided it. "Come on," he said and took her by the hand. He was still holding her hand when his father opened the door.

"Oh, so it's you." His father didn't kiss him or pat him or anything. He just looked at him real mean and then, almost friendly-like, said hello to Schultz.

"Jaimie!" his mother called from the top of the stairs. She was waiting for him to come up but he didn't move. It was lucky he hadn't because with his father staring at him like that he suddenly felt dizzy and grabbed the bannister. He sat on the bottom step and couldn't see his mother dabbing her eyes as she came down the stairs but he heard her. "Oh, how could you do such a thing to me?" and then, next to him, her voice changed,. "Jaimie, what is it?! You're not ill again?"

He's just exhausted, Madame," Schultz said. "He was pale like that in Detroit."

"Well help me, someone, get him to bed."

Jaimie's father hadn't moved but Schultz had. He picked Jaimie up and started up the stairs. Over Schultz's shoulder he saw Anna and wanted to say "Come up with us" but he was done in this time for sure and so he just smiled. Anna smiled back and called "Be careful, honey." His mother was so suprised that she missed a step and rolled her eyes.

Schultz put him on the bed and started to unlace his shoes.

"I can do the rest, Schultz," his mother said. "Jaimie's father is waiting to talk to you and he'll thank you, I'm sure, far better than I can."

She helped him undress and into his pyjamas. She said he was as white as a sheet and kept asking how he felt, if she shouldn't call Dr. Abt even though it was so late, if he didn't want her to wake Bessie to heat him up something hot. Jaimie said no, he was all right, he was just tired, but it wasn't true. His side had begun to hurt again.

"Go to sleep then, dear." She kissed him and went to the door. "Is there anything else you'd like?"

"I'd like to see Anna."

His mother stopped dead. "She must be with Schultz talking to your father. And it's so late ... it's after one."And as if two reasons weren't enough, "Do you know what sort of woman she is?"

"Yes."

"Then ... I'd really like to know ... what do you like about her?"

"Everything."

Jaimie lay there. He dozed off and then he thought he heard footsteps in the hall and Anna say, "Oh sir, I can't thank you enough." The voices were going down the stairs when she said, "But I don't like to go without telling Jaimie goodbye" and his mother said, "I'll tell him for you ... It's out of the question. You forget that he's still very very young."

Jaimie jumped up. His side really hurt so that he had to stop before going on. The outside door closed, the motor turned over and the car drove away. When he reached the hall, the lights switched off downstairs and his mother started up.

"Jaimie, what are you doing?"

"Where are they?"

"Did you think they were spending the night?" His father was

42

coming up after her. "Go to bed."

"What happened?"

"What do you think happened?" Whatever it was, it must have been bad because his father was so angry. "I paid ransom, just as if you'd been kidnapped. Isn't that what you wanted all along?"

"You don't have to yell, Edgar."

"I have to yell to get some sense in him. If he's so fond of these people, he should know what they are."

"Your father's right, Jaimie. Money was all they cared about. Why, after they got it, they didn't give a second thought to you or ..."

"That's not true. Anna asked to say goodbye to me."

"Are you calling your mother a liar?"

"I heard her."

"Well, you won't hear her again. Because the condition I made was on the understanding that they won't ever come back to – "

"Jaimie! Oh God, Edgar, call Dr. Abt."

Bessie was putting something on his tongue. The pain wasn't so bad now. The light in the corner was shaded with a towel or something. Bessie patted him and said, "Dr. Abt will be here any minute now. So don't worry, Jaimie-boy."

He wasn't worried if Dr. Abt came or not or what he'd say this time about would he die or not. He didn't care because how could he ever find Anna again, and drink bitter tea, and hear what was real from Schultz, and see the night all red, and smell perfume when she touched him and called him honey?

Solitaire

There is a picture from my boyhood that has lost its humour. It is the picture of old Mr Greenebaum, with his little legs barely touching the floor, under the Tiffany lamp playing solitaire. Whenever we boys went over to play cards at Buddy's, his father would be sitting there, and, if the layout was a good one, he would finish his game, but then he would move out, as if it were in the nature of things that we had prior rights. Perhaps he thought so because, instead of solitaire, we had come to gamble for keeps.

The picture to me was extremely funny because it seemed so incongruous: a grown man sitting alone continually playing solitaire. Then it became contemptible, perhaps at first because my parents rather despised the Greenebaums. They were members of the same community that we were, in fact many of their relatives were my parents' friends, but they lacked social flair and also, I suspect, what my mother called "civic standing". They were richer than most of us, for, besides Mr Greenebaum's leather business, Mrs Greenebaum had been an heiress, but not so much richer as to cause envy. I remember that we boys used to joke with Buddy about his wealth and now, come to think of it, I'm sure it pleased him. Certainly its manifestation, substantial and correct, showed everywhere, but without delight or much light either – as from the Tiffany lamp – and it was nowhere so apparent, or so it seemed to us, as in Buddy's room, where everything, in lieu of the usual hand-me-downs, was streamlined and expensive. Buddy too, for example, instead of one pair of initialed cuff-links, had several and these came, moreover, from some place abroad and grand, and his cuff-links box was a serious affair with velvet trays. What really impressed me, though, was his two-faced clock, half timepiece and half barometer with some kind of an embryo, pickled in alcohol, in the centre. Buddy claimed it was human. I knew then as I know now that it must have been reptilian, and yet, after all the years, I still think about it with doubt.

There was something strange about the Greenebaums anyway, as if there were a mystery or a kind of disgrace, but if there was one I never found out about it. I knew that Buddy's aunt lived up the street, with her bachelor brother, in another solid house, and that Buddy often went to see her and that no one else in our community ever did. This aunt had married outside the select circle, but on the other hand, she had become a widow, and so, with an unacceptable husband dead and buried, she should have been welcome back in the fold. Perhaps she had a lover, for if she had, in those strait-laced days, she would have been beyond recall. It was probably, however, nothing so romantic and no mystery at all, but simply the family's congenital shyness (Buddy too became a kind of recluse later) as exemplified in Mr Greenebaum's continual solitaire. Mrs Greenebaum was even more timid: she went out to shop and perhaps, secretly, to visit her sister, but otherwise, except for mealtimes, she kept to the second floor and mostly in her room. She was a sweet, stupid woman, always in black or dark blue with pearls, and she would come out on the landing to welcome us boys and then go back to her room. I think it was the welcome to the card playing that first made me cognizant of the strangeness, for when we boys played at my place or at someone else's, our parents likewise would be hospitable and show a similar approval that we all more or less stemmed from the right houses, but there would be disapproval as well, in part but mildly at the gambling (for after all our fathers gambled too), but mostly at the waste of time, and, in this respect, I can remember my mother's saying, "It's a sin to stay inside on such a beautiful day" or, as she was coquettish to the point of inviting laughter, "Aren't you boys ashamed to sit there, when there's such a wonderful exhibition at the Art Institute?" and so on. In Buddy's home there was never any suggestion of shame; on the contrary, it seemed commendable that we, the chosen heirs of the chosen few, should be there together gambling, and as if to encourage it, there were elaborate refreshments, tiny sandwiches and fresh *doboschtorte* and loganberry punch in a great silver ewer.

The despising of the Greenebaums was implicit, however, until after Mr Greenebaum's funeral, which my father attended. The house was jammed and he stood next to Edith, Mr Greenebaum's fashionable niece and they had a hard time to keep from giggling. In fact, it may have been this same funeral that caused my father to amend his last will and testament with the request that, except for the twenty-third psalm, there should be no spoken word. I remember his coming home and laughing about the rabbi's interminable eulogies, and shaking his head as he said, "You'd have thought a saint was being buried."

This framed the picture of Mr Greenebaum's playing solitaire. But it didn't end it. The picture of contempt still haunts me: a waste of time and a waste of life. For even though I do not admit it, I am becoming an old man (perhaps as old now as Mr Greenebaum when he used to sit there) and I play solitaire rather than write. I use the excuse that I am warming up to write, and it is true that in many other ways I am not like Mr Greenebaum: I have no Tiffany lamp and I like to be by the open sea. It is funnier still, I suppose, but not to me.

Even Steven

The heat. The new tent had one advantage. It was higher and the heat could circulate until dusk when it went out over the Arno Valley or wherever it went to.

The new tent was larger too. In the dreariness and sorrow there was room to file things and space means time even without relativity. There was a place now for a man to wait while the boy on duty looked up his file, and it gave Brown time to size a man up or get an impression anyway and, more important, it gave time for his system to work: the boy brought the man's file *before, not after* the man sat down. With the death messages, the awful, endless, irrefutable death messages, this was Brown's one contribution, one tempering, for with so many daily cables about so many different things it was impossible to remember the names and it had been pretty grim having a man sit down and then, if the cable had read that his wife and child had just been killed in Keokuk, not knowing why he had been sent for until after his file came.

Unless a man had initiated the contact, come for help or advice or to send a cable, they were all scared of the Red Cross Field Service. They knew that's how the death messages came. They came in controlled, though, waiting with proper-manly-military front, and Brown couldn't shorten the ordeal because he couldn't know – the Replacement Depot's complement factually meant nothing because the men were being constantly yanked out and replaced and with the boy at the desk also being continually replaced it was impossible to get an office running right and if Brown got his own little system going that was about all he could do.

The dying were even worse than the dead – with the inevitable postscript "Doctor Recommends Presence". Why, in Christ's name, did Washington send this through? Didn't they know yet that there were no emergency furloughs from the Italian Theatre? Or one, maybe, out of thousands, for with prestige there are exceptions even in the army as the rule about the rule says.

After the shock was over and the bitterness came out, Brown

47

would explain the army's point of view. After three years almost everyone – with the core of the army up from Africa – was receiving bad news from home; in three years lots of things can happen and, if the army started to let men go back, there'd be no army. It was fact and it made sense but there was another fact and another sense and Brown could never forget the boy – he was nineteen – whose wife had been killed. He was a plain, nice, good-looking boy and he had controlled both his tears and his voice when he had said, "They tell you you're fighting for your families and, Jesus, now won't they let me go back and take care of my kid?" They very seldom cried. Well then, maybe it was better for the bitterness to come out.

The old tent had had one advantage for the boys, though God knows not for the Field Director. With his own quarters on the other side of the flap, there had been a place to take a man; giving a man privacy was no little gift in the army. After the Armistice, Brown could usually get them a three-day pass to Florence and if the man's C.O. was decent or even if he wasn't he would usually let the boy's buddy, if he had one, go with him. Not that the rest-camp in Florence was any hallelujah for the bereaved G.I., but it was the attention that mattered, the idea that someone cared to arrange something against the machine.

The man who had come in and was talking to the boy hadn't been sent for because the boy made no move to try to locate a file. He was little and tough and looked about thirty. He came over and saluted. Brown returned it and said, his gesture for friendliness – no, more than a gesture – he disliked his officer status as it symbolized all that he disliked about the Red Cross, "You don't have to salute. I'm not an officer, I only wear this monkey-suit. Sit down."

It was a quick way to break the ice. This man was pleasantly shocked as you are by the surprise of wit under the dirt of a good joke. He showed it in the corners of his eyes and mouth but he had something else on his mind. He sat down and fished around in the inside pocket of his field-jacket. He peered down in this pocket as if it were the black, bottomless pit of a well. Finally he pulled out the letter he was looking for and put it on the desk in front of Brown. He said nothing.

48

Brown had been waiting for some word, some explanation, and against his fractional hesitancy the man said abruptly,

"You're the Red Cross Field Director, aren't you?"

"I'm the Assistant Field Director."

"Read it."

Brown did. It was a wonderful letter. The woman, this man's wife, had become pregnant. She admitted that she had done wrong. She wrote that she had worked until her pregnancy was about to show and then she had left town with their two children. Her husband's parents, she said, would not be disgraced because they would know nothing about it.

She said that her husband could divorce her if he wanted to but he mustn't be misled into thinking that he could ever get their children away from her. She said she perhaps loved him still, she didn't know, it was different after the children came, maybe she loved them more.

Yes, she wrote, she had unquestionably done wrong but she reminded him that he had been no angel: when he had gone AWOL it had meant that for months she and the children had received no allotment and it was she who had had to work to support them.

She couldn't help what his parents wrote him; he ought to know them by now and know her and whom to believe. Yes, sure, she drank once in a while, but not often because in the first place she didn't have the money. Nor the time.

She added that she guessed maybe she couldn't be so awfully old yet either because two boys on a truck the other day had whistled at her.

At the end of the letter, she thanked him for the flowers.

Brown looked at the man. "If you don't want her," he said, "I'll take her."

The man had evidently been prepared for a Red Cross Christer. He was again shocked – and delighted. But he still said nothing. Instead he dug down in that pocket again and produced another letter. In handing it his gesture said, "You have passed the first test fine; try this."

The second letter was from the same girl and said the same thing. It added one new phase. She said her husband was so goddam stubborn. But in her attack, love as well as anger came out clear and strong and Brown felt that these people must have had great pleasure in sex and more besides, Eros had sometimes been there too. And again she ended her letter so nicely. She said she guessed maybe she was stubborn too.

"How old are you?" said Brown.

"Twenty-four."

"And your wife?"

"Twenty-four."

"Well," Brown said, borrowing the man's poker-face, "what do you want me to do about it?"

"I want to know what you think."

"Are you thinking about a divorce?"

"I was thinking about it."

"We're not a divorce court," said Brown, still deadpan, and gave the little spiel from the orientation course: why the Red Cross couldn't intervene, the delicacy, the technicalities, the two sides to every quesion, that divorce was a legal matter.

"What would you do?" said the man.

"I'm not supposed to give advice," said Brown, preparing to give it. "And anyway, how can I tell you or anyone else what to do?

"But I can tell you one thing: don't listen to all the big talk in your tent, what the boys would do if anyone ever touched their women. They don't know nothing from nothing – or anyway the ones who talk don't – they don't know what their women are doing and neither do I. But this much we do know: your wife's no tramp. Because if she were, she'd have known more about it and would never have got caught."

The man liked it. But nevertheless he had been wronged and didn't want Brown on his wife's side.

"I was sore at her before I went away," he said. "I wanted her to come down to camp for the weekend, you know, before we went to embarkation. But she wouldn't come, she said she couldn't afford it. That's not right, is it? She was drawing a hundred and ten dollars and I was getting only ten. She could have come."

"I think she should have come too," Brown said, "whether she wanted to or not. She wasn't smart about it, that's all. Lots of woman have to pretend right after a child is born."

The man got it, nearly.

50

"Look," said Brown, "I have a friend in Tennessee. He's married and they have four kids and they get along together fine. But he told me once that every time, right after his wife was pregnant, he was sure she didn't want him to touch her until over a year after the child was born. That's a long time. Only she's an intelligent woman and she always pretended. Your wife's intelligent too, only she didn't know that, see? She's young, that's all. And besides, she's honest.

"But you're all wrong about the money. A hundred and ten dollars isn't so damn much for a wife and two small kids. And don't forget your food, rent and clothes are paid for. It's about fair."

The man had never thought about it that way before. But he said again, "what would *you* do?"

"I think you love her," said Brown, surprising himself also by the sudden sweet word laid there in the khaki dirt. " Otherwise why would you send her flowers? That's a lot of dough to cable flowers out of ten dollars a month."

The man almost smiled.

"I can't tell you what to do because I don't know. I don't know how it will work out. But why don't you wait until you get back? What the hell that you've got a child that doesn't belong to you? What difference does it make so long as nobody knows it? Everybody's got something – and you've got so much more than most people have, maybe you can work something out together. Most people will never know enough to work anything out, you know that.

"Write her that you're going to wait. Only don't put her on her good behaviour. You've been no angel either, so make it fifty-fifty. But you've got to start over again, just like you did before – if you can't send her flowers, send her flowers in the way you write her. She wants to be whistled at.

"She"ll come along and then everything'll be fine. And if she doesn't, then you don't want her anyway. But I think she will."

The man sat there, his pride wrapped up again in a brand new package. He was in the driver's seat again too and Brown felt once more that he was lucky to have this girl and that somehow he would have her.

The man rose and paid off. He didn't say anything and he didn't salute – he put out his hand and smiled.

51

John Brown in Rome

The river flows yellow and barren. The water of purity is blue. Clear water and the water of longing: over the sea is ever the land's fairest way. Something old and something new.

Even Peter means stone. His stones, now the church's, once the river's were lifted, soaked first like all transplantings – his in martyrs' blood – by another bridgebuilder – Nero this time – but long before that we are told on the very same site there was human sacrifice to Cybele. The blood is in the wine, that is all, the shrines are the same. Why, there lares torches burned at night now candles light or watt-bulbs blight the madonna, in the very same niches, upon my honour.

The tourist comes as he always came, or so he says, to light the candles and see the sights. But more than that, in the temples or out, he comes to catch an image by the river, to take a sounding in the paydirt and measure out his proper span against the shadow of eternal dust. In Keokuk as in Rome it is the best reason of all for leaving home.

John Brown of Iowa went riding to the sea or, in the dawn's early light, went walking to the river. With him walked victory for he had beaten the sun. In the ancient stone he saw the eagles, Roman, Holy Roman, Russian, Prussian, ours, and in the rockets' red glare heard the scream, not of victory but of its revenue and deceit; he was no longer a boy and knew about the intoxication of drums on parade. Still there is much to be said for intoxication and he was enjoying his.

Walking down the Via Panisparna there is the time and the circumstance and the purpose.

The time is dawn. Only the dispossessed picking in the refuse are up to greet it, an anomaly of cities, as if the dispossessed alone have the courage to meet another day.

The circumstance is the priest. Coming from the Piazza del Grillo John Brown caught him watching cats copulate. There was nothing

52

funny about it. The priest, what's more, stood his ground and to John's look of disgust turned his eyes heavenward, from habit probably more than subterfuge. "Ah, ha, I caught you," John had wanted to say but he didn't say it. The priest brought his look back from heaven and met John's full on. "There was an ancient mariner," but the priest didn't say it either. He was the dispenser and not the receiver and for this John should have had admiration and pity too but the priest's eyes were glazed like a cow's.

John Brown's purpose is to write down what he knows by the bridges of time.

In a sense his life had been a preparation for this purpose and he was moving at last. But there are sideroads on the way to anywhere. None of the roads are marked, either, because nature abhors a vacuum or because all the signposts would read the same: But for the Grace of God. One such road is the flyer's, lovely with the cushioned leaves of tactile values, the pleasure of rubbing differences, the approach to death.

I packed my trunk for Saratoga and put in .... yes, but what did you take out? You can't take out remembrance.

I remember mamma. I remember mamma combing her hair, her lovely hair. And mamma said, "I won't live long, dear." Only mamma didn't keep her promise. She lived always saying dear, giving love, monkey-love.

Or I remember mamma (someone else's or mine, no matter) when she was dying. They sent me for the doctor and it was dark and I was afraid and turned back and I was ashamed.

But every child is afraid of the dark, is afraid that mamma will die or that mamma won't. Why do you worry? I do not worry and yet the thing is there.

As well as feeling one evokes rules, spontaneously, on purpose, at random, in desperation. One says the higher the species, the less the instinct. Of course this rule was not made up by a worm. Another says the younger the child, the fuller the memory or a straight line is the shortest distance. Hence perhaps the fear of birth and why the bright child always so astounds us.

But what will you remember, really remember, at thirty or at fifty? Will you remember me?

I remember nothing. It is not senility, it is that there has been so much to remember covered with the wrinkled leaves of feeling. I remember what I have been told, events without feeling. Still the leaves are not dead, their veins can be quickened; I can evoke the feeling, otherwise I should be dead.

John Brown remembered mamma – and papa too. He remembered the time he knocked over the egg-cup and mamma was angry. Then papa, accidentally on purpose, knocked over his egg-cup and mamma cried. That time papa was on his side, the beginning of the triangle, writ in indelible ink (like a rule) but in white, to be deciphered later yet always there even after the deciphering, the pattern for red shoes, for two boys and a girl, for the boys milling around Alcibiades, for a man and two woman, for separation, for the doublecross play from Tinkers to Everts to Chance. Only it takes three outs to end the ballgame and so there is one to go – which is the part of the story about Pandora that everyone remembers.

John Brown remembered Helen Shepherd's house in Chicago but the house only vaguely. It was a walk-up in the just-off-the-respectable district and Helen supposedly didn't have out-and-out prostitutes but married women who wanted to make a little dough on the side. John used to go there with the older boys but he didn't do anything. He played cards with Helen in the parlor.

It is strange but the same happened to Tommy Montagne, who also came from a big house and was maybe once a poet, out with cowhands near Butte, Montana. They used to take Tommy in too when he was a kid and he also liked what seemed the atmosphere of reality after the trumpery of home. And he didn't do anything either then but later he left his wife and their little girl whom he loved for the girls and poetry of Paris. (He didn't find the poetry, though).

John Brown went back to Helen's alone when he was twenty. He had a wonderful girl, young and Italian and beautiful. Maybe she

54

had been more excited because he was from the other side of the tracks or because she knew that he had never been with a girl. Anyway he always remembered her lying there with her breasts and all so lush in the summer's heat and he couldn't figure it out at all then why he had been such a fool that night as to take the train back to the triangle because the other players were expecting him. It was a sealing of an appointment with time called compulsion.

Before that John remembered his seduction. Every child whose quality of love is strained wants to be seduced, so it is almost every child. It is a desire not so much to satisfy the craving of the flesh as the need for attention, because the attention in seduction is genuine, that is, the child knows that the seducer wants the child for his own sweet sake with no strings tied. John waited until highschool and then began to prowl in Washington Park. It was an exciting place all right at dusk with Negroes, gandydancers, ball players, God knows who all. The police must have left it alone in those days because they were busy elsewhere, Anyway there was nothing pleasant about the seduction. John still remembered the nasty story the man told him and then bingo he was seduced and shocked and chagrined and resigned to the loss of childhood perhaps or the beginning of the endless search for the apples of Hesperides.

John Brown remembered what mamma said – too well. She heard the wheels of progress like regimentation along the speedways that follow the flatlands and she knew the sideroad to her local Gods. At any Four Corners they are similar and yet as the land still tells beyond the speedways they are as separate as their sacred hills. Mamma's were very powerful not only because of their material power but because she herself became one of them.

Mamma's Four Corners was the Upper Jewish Set in Chicago. It had glamor because Jews have a maybe innate appreciation of elegance and also because its women were so beautiful. Indeed the visa for entry besides fashion which meant money and some breeding was beauty. It was a kind of pre-myth society, where the real powers were all goddesses who in some blind way had set up a king-dictator who in turn took from the goddesses his paramours. His name was Mel Nathan and in the formulative years of Mount

Olympus his goddess-paramour was Flo Stettenheimer. What she did and what she wore was what they did and what they wore which again became the actions and attributes of the Gods.

The telephone calls all day Friday and Saturday morning too about what Aphrodite-Flo would wear Saturday on Mount Olympus (Country Club Elysian Fields) – an evening dress or a sportsdress and hat? Better take both as Flo was fickle. And the summer when they all wore evening dresses with great black tulle hats. Elsie Marxwell put a red rose in hers but it was considerd bad taste. And one Saturday mamma tried a gold hat but she never tried it again.

Mamma had a gift for wearing hats and therefore risked mistakes. Once in a car riding to Olympus she had doubts about an expensive one and asked Blanche, who also really knew. "Oh Maggie," Blanche had said, "Every woman has a row of lemons on her shelf every season."

What they said and who they were and what they did: the acts and names were fixed by pride. Like the Greeks', all the goddesses were lovely, either tall and thin or perfect thirty-sixes. Mel Nathan's wife, Alma, was Hera but there was no bickering. Apparently she didn't know that she was being deceived because when Mel died she said that on that score she had never had to worry. But then, after Mel died, she was dethroned.

The really great goddesses of Olympus in the stabilizing years were Aphrodite-Flo and tall Blanche and Gertie. Gertie together with some of the others came down from a pre-Hellenic pantheon. That is, she was an Emmanuel Fish heir. Emmanuel Fish had made his money in the early packing days in Chicago, probably in kosher meat but no matter, and it was said that he couldn't even write his name. Be that as it may, like descendants of other robber barons, these Emmanuel Fish heirs had drive. And yet not all of them were chosen for the Fast Set or inner sanctum of the primary Gods. Gertie had married a man with the slow motion of old-world courtesy and still he was not well-born. Their marriage was the protoype for a recipe that mamma was forever using about everyone, "She has social position and he has money" or vice versa. In Gertie's case it was both vice and versa as she had been rich before her marriage but her husband, so they said, had by reinvestment made her vastly richer. She had the finest strands of pearls to be seen in the Middlewest. Not that they could be seen very often because she only wore them to the opera and to Mount Olympus.

She took on some of the attributes of Apollo, becoming a kind of goddess of music on the side, that is, she became a patroness of the open-air opera at Ravinia, which was very nice in summer when besides the music you could hear the Chicago and Milwaukee trains go by. Gertie had a box there of course but, as there were only twenty couples in the Fast Set and most of them were bored with opera anyway, tall Blanche once asked her how she filled her box. "Oh," said Gertie, "Sometimes I ask my friends and sometimes I ask interesting people." She was always correct. Mamma said that Gertie and Alma-Hera were ladies, meaning that mamma was too and probably likewise implying that Gertie and Alma-Hera would never sleep around among the twenty husband-gods as the other goddesses were beginning to do. Even so Gertie wore extremely low-cut evening dresses with only tulle sometimes below the cleft-line. Tulle was important then. She was immensely fashionable and used to go to New York for three weeks twice each year. Her ritual, like many another moon-goddesses', had three phases: the first week she never bought but just looked to see what was best; the second week she bought; and the third week she fitted. It was said that she spent between ten and twelve thousand each year not counting furs and that tall Blanche did too and some of the others. This was considered the norm for the well-dressed woman but most of the goddesses had to rough it on less and this caused suffering and strife.

Tall Blanche was also immensely fashionable and lots of fun and absolutely amoral, not so much in the sense of sexual immorality, but it is doubtful if she ever thought of anything besides her own immediate pleasure. She had been born a Bing. The Bings had made their money early in clothing and the children all had a great flair for clothes and Provence country-houses and foreign cars and the boys also for foreign mistresses. Nevertheless at the beginning only Blanche made the inner circle of the Fast Set even though her younger sister was eminently presentable and the best golfer on Olympus and had married the youngest bank president in the

Middlewest and they had the smartest cars of all, grey-black phaetons with orange wheels. Her sister and her husband, the bank president, were in the Slow Set. The Slow Set was on the whole younger than the Fast Set and on Saturday nights at Elysian Fields had a table next to the Fast Set's and they democratically danced with each other sometimes but for many years they didn't really go together except on rare occasions. The Slow Set was a kind of proving ground for the Fast Set. Mel, the king, every few years would get out his accolade and touch someone and this couple would then move over or rather up to the Fast Set. This finally happened to Blanche's sister and her husband, which was lucky because he had publicly said that if it didn't happen, bank or no bank, he would leave Chicago. But it wasn't just money that decided it by any means. It was something miraculous like with all Gods.

Because the richest man in the club never approached the Fast Set. He was a kindly man too and when he died left a great fortune to the poor. In the end one of his daughters apogamously made it but he never got near. Anyway, one Saturday night, this man had a family party at Olympus and for it requisitioned the Tudor living-room that otherwise would have been the after-dinner ballroom. There was a little balcony overlooking this room and from time to time during the evening members of the Fast Set, having been dispossessed of their merrymaking hall, went out on this balcony and looked *down*. When mamma went out, she found there the mother of one of the goddesses, a very ugly little woman who knew all about European watering places and French dressmakers. Suddenly this woman turned to mamma and said, "It's like looking at a bunch of niggers, isn't it?" Mamma was terribly shocked. She thought it was altogether unkind. But she was terribly pleased too because mamma had not originally come from Chicago and her entry, like many another on Olympus, had been hard won and this was, as it were, out of the mouths of babes, signifying that she was ensconced with her godhead a family by-word.

Still the Gods changed form time to time, some elevated and some demoted, which may explain why the Greek Gods are so hard to remember. The deification of the Weinsteins, for example, was absolutely astounding – why, they were never in the Slow Set

58

at all! To begin with, neither Eloise nor Frank Weinstein came from Chicago and neither of them had "background". It was even rumored – but in all fairness it bordered on the incredible – that she had been born in Brooklyn. Wherever she was born though, she had the makings of a goddess. She was Titian-haired and lovely and her sweet-scented drapes in Diana-pastel outpointed the goddesses' very own; they came from Paris and were so fine that you never thought of the yearly stipend. This was probably because she didn't either, her husband owning most of the sulphur this side of hell. Now the Fast Set knew of the Weinsteins in the sense that they had an almost bowing acquaintance with the other hundred and fifty members at Elysian Fields and it must be admitted that on occasion some of them had even accepted invitations chez les Weinsteins to dine. The bait was culture with a capital K. For Frank and Eloise gave lavishly to the University of Chicago and therefore its president likewise came to dine. This was the kind of prestige that ordinarily might have enticed all the Gods but the trouble was that the University of Chicago was nothing new to most of them. The Marxwells, owners of a large department store and among whose descendants there were several Gods, had given a Gothic Hall to the University a generation before, and Gertie-Thalia had been a member of its first class to graduate women. And more important still, Mel, the king, together with his brother, were Yale men and therefore naturally had very little use really for a rural university. Nevertheless, prestige on earth is the life-blood of those who rule from heaven, and, besides, several of the primaries, particularly mamma and Gertie, were civic minded and they reported that the Weinsteins were not only fine hosts but that "she" was altogether charming. Yet all this and the University too was not enough. What did the trick, although fortuitously, was the Weinstein Collection. For not so quietly Frank and Eloise had been plucking Venetian plums, including a delectable Bellini, perhaps the ripest Veronese outside of Venice and a bevy of Tiepolos, these last doubtless to give the old game new zip. This concentration on Venetian, furthermore, in some subtle way stressed Frank's adoration of his own Titian-haired, for he was notoriously fond of girls. His two-time collecting at any rate gave Aphrodite-Flo material for perhaps her greatest mot, to wit: "She

59

has Old Masters and he young mistresses." The quip was repeated so often that, like the handwritng of old, it must have been inscribed (this time in all likelihood by repercussion) on the very walls of Parnassus. In any event it brought the Weinsteins incessantly to the lips of the Fast Set ad then, bingo like seduction, Mel's accolade was out and they were in.

But when a god or goddess was in, they were in. All else, even Brooklyn was forgotten; the apotheosis itself was purification and the new gods automatically became the best friend of every other god and goddess. So it is now and ever has been from the beginning.

But not will be. For when a god or goddess was demoted, which happened rarely because of divorce or the disgrace of misfortune, it was as cruel and quick as the punishment of Zeus. Oh this old best friend, of a certainty, would be talked to – almost warmly – if met on the street, but never again invited. The way of the gods is always a mystery to mortals.

The fear of demotion was as strong with mamma as the pride of place. Now surely Zeus, the patricide, must have had this same fear, for we are told of his awe of the Erinnyes, to whom, although unwelcome on Olympus, he still acknowledged precedence of birth. Mamma and her goddess-sisters too had their Erinnyes, who although likewise unwelcome on Olympus, could often be found in the guise of old crones if you surprised a goddess at her toilette. Like Zeus', they had come down from of old – from a goddess's maiden phase. Mamma's was Minnie Stamm. She was a distant cousin of papa but this was of little consequence; of far greater importance was her girlhood friendship with both Aphrodite-Flo and Gertie-Thalia; and most important of all was her marriage, for by it, even before the dawn of the gods, Minnie had been earmarked for Olympus. Her husband, "Cousin" Leo, in that distant past called chaos, had been all elegance and family and wealth too, in fact the eon's catch. However, with the creation, as everyone knows, the destiny of god and man became inseparable. Zeus' thunderbolt struck. In the San Francisco earthquake – or rather in the holocaust that followed – nothing surely was more lasting in horror than the fear it burned in mamma's heart. For Cousin Leo had been a Fire Insurance President. Still, for years afterwards, Minnie hung on as the goddess crossed her humble threshold for baked grapefruit and hearts of palm until, finally, hearts of palm went out and the goddesses one by one fell off, finding the long ride to the South Side (no longer fashionable) more and more tiring. But not mamma. She went in loyalty and fear. Because although papa with his law practice was not, like many of the gods, vulgarly "in trade", he was a more or less happy speculator on the side. He had a great gift for making money but none at all for keeping it with the result that, as in the days of old, the fat years were followed by the lean – but in continual rotation. In the lean years mamma put up a brave front but she constantly complained that she "hadn't been brought up to be a gambler's wife" and that what she hated most "was the pretense". When asked why she bothered, she would answer that she did it "for papa's sake". Which was in part at least true. In fairness to papa, though, during the fat years – and with the normal stipend – mamma always said that "papa was pretty smart". But as the stockmarket is never stable, so mamma never lost a fear of fate worse than death, i.e., of being left like poor Minnie Stamm.

Somehow, somewhere along the line, poor Minnie's werewolf mated with Little Red Ridinghood's grandmother and its whelp was more hideous than Echidna's hound. For, besides tales from the local gods, mamma told the story of the boy who cried wolf to fool the other shepherds, who would come running, and then, on the day when the wolf came, no shepherd heard his cry. This story scared the living daylights out of us. Nor could the really great misfortune that we happened to have a pack of cousins actually named Wolf who, furthermore, were both hairy and ravenous, altogether account for such a tortuous fear of death. Because the fact was that the awful story's moral had never been lost on mamma either, who therefore told it with feeling. She was forever proclaiming her own truthfulness so that long before we had heard of The Player Queen we knew a meaning for "methinks the lady doth protest too much" and we knew too, had mamma been the little shepherd, she might well have cried "Oh!Oh!" or "Look! See!" but then when the shepherds came running she would have protested with all her singleness of childish purpose that she had "never said the word 'wolf'." Nor could we ever catch her out, nor was she ever eaten.

Coming down the ramp from the Piazza del Grillo, John Brown sang,

"Bury your dead," the pirate said.
"But your dead are buried at sea."
"Then bury your dead," the pirate said,
"Under a juniper tree.
"The corpse neath the copse
"Will ferment the hops –"
"To brew up another tea?"
"And nourish your crops"
"To be shot by the cops,"
Laughed the pi-i-rate glee-ee-fully.

He was not in voice but his rhythm was good and the cats in Trajan's Market below didn't seem to mind. Indeed one part-Persian, having made a kind of loge on the second tier (but with no tiara), blinked approval. Doubtless they would all politely clap, John Brown thought, if they only could. "A matin is a matin," he said, for the day had not yet begun, "and I will sing you another:

Beware of the interpreters
Whoever they may be: of the
Navigator- cartographer
Who never climbed a mast at sea;
Of the Phrygian-robed priest-orator
Who's no nearer Christ than me;
Of parents wise with focused eyes
So children's eyes won't see.
Go to the source, Miss de la Mar,
Whatever it may be."

This time the cats did applaud, wildly although the sound of their little paws was less audible than the tapping of kid at a ladies' afternoon concert. Even so the success almost made John Brown lose his head but he had had some theatrical training and knew trick of saving up for a finale. He therefore only bowed.

A Room in Rome

The room was noble and as nobility had been its intention it was a success. It was not quite beautiful. Still it was elegant in a way and it had character and charm and, all in all, quality, and so we are back again to noble.

The room had more meaning to an American than such fantasies as playing president or helping weary men. Because it may be that an American more than all others appreciates ancient nobility. And more than nobility, the ancient. He needs to see it sometimes, the assurance of the beauty sometimes made by man to endure or almost endure or anyway endure more than man can. All ancient things are not this beauty and whether beautiful or not are mostly here by chance, but all ancient proportions recall or invoke this beauty and so refresh the soul.

But nevertheless what impressed Eggibab most of all in this room had nothing to do with it. It was the cheval glass. The cheval glass went so far back that Eggibab didn't see it for years and yet it was there sometimes in the corner reflecting the room, sometimes out a little reflecting from the casements on the living sea, reflecting his lovely wife but never reflecting him. Why?

Why was it noble? It was noble because it was part of a *piano nobile,* that is, it was in the main line of a great palace. It was noble also on account of its proportions and again on account of its size for although it was by no means one of the rooms of state, as a bedroom it was tremendous. But it was wrong in time. It was renaissance but late, too late and so like its palace always wanting to be something else but not really wanting, not wanting enough to change. It was hard to judge because it had such an elegant name; you were bamboozled by it like a painter by a colour or a poet by a word or a boy by a girl or vice versa, and other things too, like a snob, and also a historian by a name, the most elegant name of all, really, in Rome after the decline and fall or roughly A.D. and i.e., Caetani. Even so no one called it "a beautiful palace". Nevertheless it had distinction over against the other more beautiful name-palaces because in this one everyone, including the ancient Caetanis, worked.

Now is work the one great distinction? It is the time of the Hungarian massacres and likewise high noon, the place is the Prince's table although it is the Princess who invites people, and the talk is as advertised. Now the old Prince, bless him, is more deaf than not and after trying to listen, half-listening and not listening at all to the buzz buzz buzz, he suddenly dove right in. "Oh yes," he agreed, "the Russians are terrible., You cannot believe a word they say. My mother always warned me..." And without a flicker he was back and we with him to pony carts with the Tabloievski children (what have I spawned?) against whom the Prince's dear mother had so kindly warned him. Yet the Prince at eighty-five worked polishing and repolishing *Isola del Sole (Island of the Sun* at eighty-five, think of that!), an old opera to be sure but to be performed again, this time by air from Radio Milan. And the Princess worked, and the care of her editing and the mechanics of her publishing went on in and from the palace. And the young Princess – now almost fifty – in the shadow of her parents and the deeper shadow of their Victorian promise and in the black shadow of humiliation, for the ancient line would die with her – took her father to the country where she tended her fantastic garden and brought her father back to the city where she directed his library (also in the palace), only Caetani documents but nonetheless a record of the western world from back before Charlemagne with one parchment made out to Caetani by the Emperor himself. And the hero of this story wrote in the palace and his wife painted there and together they raised their children. This activity kept the palace in spite of its bulk, in spite of reminders of the avarice that had built it (the rhymes are popes, hopes, palaces, phalluses, heirs, theirs) more free than not from that feeling of hot-house oppression which palaces often generate.

But the room. Well, yes, the room – the room was large indeed with two elaborate doors, two tremendous windows and a great, distant, blue, unbelievable ceiling. The doors, like the windows with their two sets of shutters, were double, that is, folding both inside and out; they faced the room with mirrors and were at either end and directly opposite in the way of old palaces which are in good part glorified halls. They were immensely ornate with scrolls, some painted and more chiselled, and at tea on rainy Sundays would not have been too outmoded with their grandchildren at Versailles. The walls were of the same lighter green, tan-apple and sick at heart. What saved the colour was first of all the dirt, for in a rich room dirt can be an asset, and the insistence of both doors and ceiling. This ceiling also had greens and faded gold but it was firmly based on cobalt; great spirals in stuccoed trompe-l'oeil ran around connecting animals in signet frames, one to each wall. The spirals went on and up to better things, to a faun and his lady about to, then maybe having done for he was sulky and they were back to back, and then sitting alone and possibly thinking about it again; around them and among them was an infinity of caryatids, griffins, noids, cornucopias and fretwork, grotesques and arabesques that had come from Persia. From the central cartouche, now framing nothing, there hung the stump of a cord, but once there had been a crest and this same cord had held a chandelier to make it blaze. Altogether it was a rather hideous ceiling and yet it was wonderful, too, because lying on the bed at night, year in and year out, you couldn't make out what all the shouting was about, there was nothing to hold you long enough, and so it was exactly what a painted ceiling ought to be.

There was also the fireplace. Its enamel face was so white, so washed and so clean that it seemed as unrelated to the high festooning and the bilious colour as hospital enamel to pleasure and pain. It was framed with blackish marble trimmed in dying gold but it was nevertheless surprising and friendly because its size was almost human. Near it, and in deference perhaps, an ordinary door had been cut through to the corridor beyond. Between the fireplace and the door there was a wood stove, a kind common in Rome, made of vertical, different-sized box-shaped tiers. Originally these stoves are white but this one had been painted matching green. Its stack went up and up, way up above sea level until it turned to go half-way over the mantle where it turned again, exactly centred, to enter the flue. It was ridiculous on every count – because of its plain speaking in among the curlicues, because of the pipe like an idiot's feather and because the place now had steam – and yet some master craftsman had so squarely placed it that it still seemed functional. And it was functional but for another reason: its absurdity was a friendly reminder against what otherwise might have been an invitation to pretension.

The furniture, following the mixed leads of painted splendour and period heating, was a not unhappy mixture of former Caetani glory, former tenants' neglect and their own (viz., hero and heroine's) fine taste. There were three or four Caetani pieces around the room, a commode, a desk and two bedside consoles, all heavy, antique, inlaid and of no period; there were the former tenants' entries: a cheval glass, a Victorian coat-hanger and no one knew if the centre settee and chairs, red plush and brocade, unmatching and broken down, were Caetani or not; it didn't matter as they waited comfortably around a table on the red aubusson in front of the hearth. Their red decay was as right with the aubusson as the rug was with the ceiling. For the present tenants, in addition to pictures, lamps, books and a great box-bed, had added the rug and in point of fact Eggibab Cheever, for such is our hero's name, had given it to his wife for Christmas for the second-best reason for giving a wife anything, viz., he had wanted it himself. The choice of this rug for this room, however, had been such pure straight unadulterated genius that every time Eggibab saw it – and if you consider that he has slept in the room for several years it adds up to quite a few times – he was amazed not only by the insane precision of his choice but by the fact that tourists continued to flock to the nearby forum while none came to see the ruby red under the cobalt blue. Of course Eggibab realized that these tourists didn't know about the rug and if they had they probably would not have appreciated it unless told to do so by a guide who in turn would have had to have been told.

One could smell the sea in such a room, looking out from its casement windows on a distant sea, and then the black sails and blinds closed, for disappointment, for betrayal, for a life gone by in seclusion.

In the mornings at two, three, or four there was relief from the traffic noise beyond the bombed wall separating the house from the sea, but not for long, and never silence. Then you could hear the clock strike from the Campidoglio, the head and centre of the world. At night, too, the rains came from over the hills as in the country. There was always one more late car for love or murder, the distant tooting, the compressed malaise, the city sweating, pulling at its seams. "If I were president," Eggibab then thought, "I would work for an hour of silence – Greenwich time – over the great wide world. Then the strife would stop, oh at great material cost and also to life, for in that one hour no ambulance could shriek its way in pain. But in that hour man might think, just think and even maybe feel again."

Eggibab did not play *If I were President* often. He dreamt of other things, of Imperial cruelty and Etruscan kings, of the unbroken chain of Roman time and how to hold it in his hand, to feel the beat from here, where even before recorded time the city's heart never quite stopped pumping. Can one tell it all? One can dream to tell it all and a princely room is wide and high.

A Halo in the Hand

After the long drive down, the children for once had gone willingly to bed but Jake was still exhausted. The bath had revived him but not enough. Coming into the room he slowly, wearily registered Maria's fresh faint make-up.

"Tired?" she said.

"Well...."

"Of course you are," Maria said with her accustomed generosity. "Well, stop rattling around then and come to sleep."

She looked tired too and a little wan. It was his fault no doubt ... "A woman tended is a woman blooming." Now he always had an excuse: a cold, a pain, fatigue, the children in the adjoining room with no key at Urbino, or, in Venice, the children again or Bobby and Dominique staying on too late in their room. Well, what did she want at his age, a movie-hero? It was easy for a woman: she can pretend. Still, he felt rotten about it.

"You should sleep late, Jake," Maria said, kissing him, "and then begin to work."

He pulled tight. Not that he should have, not that she was needling him, but *work* was the sensitive place. He should have let it go but he didn't.

"I can't sleep late. I'm going to the country with Bobby."

"Oh."

"There's a house he knows about or went to the last time he and Dominique played here. He doesn't know if it's empty but it's only about an hour out of Rome."

"I should have thought you'd have had enough of them after the trip and with Bobby's party too tomorrow night."

"I don't have too much of Bobby. Besides they leave the next day."

"Isn't Dominique going?"

"I didn't ask him. Would you like to come?"

"No," Maria said. She laughed.

"Are you sore?"

"No, darling. I was thinking Dominique will never be able to

68

take it – you're taking Bobby off alone plus his party."

"You don't think I should go?"

"Oh, Jake, I want you to work, that's all. You should go if you want. Maybe a house is a solution. And you're right if they're leaving. Who knows? – they may not even come back this way from Athens or wherever they're going. I just thought it was always something but of course you're right. Good night, darling."

"Good night."

Although Bobby had only been to Anticoli once, on a previous tour with Dominique some three years before, he led Jake straight to it – off the provincial road, off the road that climbed up to the town, down the little Roman road and then up the grass lane to where it stopped below the hill. There they could see the house in the oak grove above the ledge.

As they climbed up the path, Bobby had been right too about his little lecture on distance. "If you can find it near a city – I don't mean that I like urban country any better than you do – it's foolish to go too far away. It's not only that if you should get bored, but it's no effort to get here." It made such pertinent sense that Jake suspected Maria had rehearsed him. But as they climbed up and over the ledge and as the place was so beautiful, Jake thought that it made no difference if she had. Bobby spoke for him. "I could be happy here," he said and sat down on what once must have been a lawn above the ledge. He was worn out, not from the climb but from the layoff right in the middle of his concert tour with Dominique. For this reason perhaps he went on talking. "I like this country even better than Tuscany or Umbria. There you feel that every tree has been planted for Piero or somebody to paint. But here it's a little more rugged, a little more real. All ready for you, Jake."

"As a matter of fact, all the terrible painters at the turn of the century used to come here."

"Then you can show what they missed."

"They didn't miss the women, I guess. Did you know that the models for all those erotic ladies around the Piazza Esedra came from here?"

"No," Bobby said. "Maybe we'd better walk up to the town." But he made no move. "I didn't know that this house would be empty either. It's funny but I don't remember a thing about the inside. It looks as ..."

"As if no one has been here since that day?"

"Wouldn't it be wonderful if they hadn't? I'd be so happy if I'd done something for you after all you and Maria are always doing for Dominique and me. I always mean to give a speech about it, to thank you properly, but you never let me."

"Give a speech now" Jake walked over to the ledge. He was listening to Bobby but at the same time he was thinking of the time when he had first toured Italy and spent a night at La Verna. He had been very young and very taken with St. Francis. He had begun the *Little Flowers* because he had been told that the Italian was so easy but he had gone on delighted with the simple purity, and although anything but a Catholic he had been tempted to give up what someday would be his not so modest riches for the good life. In a way, from his social city-Jewish background, not to mention the fleshy side of nature, it had been ridiculous and yet it hadn't been either, for that's what more or less all the Elishas and Elijahs had been, and for that matter all the New Testament entries as well. Nevertheless La Verna, even though he had not retired to a little brother's hut, had made him feel all the more the power of St. Francis because after all the years the shrine was inviolate – no gilt, no hush-hush, no neon signs. Just the wood on the pointed plateau, pointing up as if to God. No wonder Francis had had or felt he had had the stigmata there. Sinai likewise, Jake had thought then, must have pointed up too.

"I can't give a speech now that you frame it. But Dominique and I are really grateful because I'm not so sure that we could have gone on without you. Every time there's a crisis – and there always seems to be a crisis – you and Maria come through. I hope we're all right after this tour – that is if we live through this tour – but we've thought that before and the concert business, let alone the problem of two pianos, is hell. But it's not only the money. I mean this time, like arranging the hotel, taking us on the trip, everything."

"We love you."

"Your speech was better than mine," Bobby said and got up.

"I'm sorry though about the party tonight."

"Why?"

"Oh, it's a real nuisance for Maria."

"She thinks your birthday only comes once a year."

"It's beyond the line of duty. Shouldn't we walk around? Dear God, look at the daffodils. There must be other wonderful flowers here."

There were.

Since that day when Jake had first seen the house at Anticoli, negotiated for it through the lawyer in Rome, hired Antonio and Antonetta, set them to cleaning the pools and putting the water to running again, brought out a bed, a stove and other essentials, one month had gone by. In that month the bloom of daffodils had withered, the fruit and lilacs had blossomed and faded and, as a result of heavy rains in the wake of a cold winter, a small flood had also come and gone in the valley below. These showy acts of nature, both usual and unusual, had surprised him. Not that he had forever been a stranger to the land nor that he hadn't been aware of it in the distance, but from the compulsion of the city he had accepted the land as a static idea and taken *The Book of Hours* as.. well… the stuff of poetry.

Spring with its pastoral rites, now as then, is of course the stuff of poetry, all the more so viewed from the tricks of success, from the ready money or the slow drudge, from the pull of sex in the easy flesh and the more easy telling. But from this house in the country the land was something in its own right beyond even the display of the *bella stagione*, a promise of peace and of something more – a use of peace perhaps, of contemplation.

The house itself, at least inside, was a horror with bare stone floors and colder fireplaces. But outside in vine-covered balconies and porticos it gave to the world – like a creed – the semblance of grace. Perhaps it was better ugly for its position was so choice. Under the town and yet high on its own hill, from behind its secrecy of oaks and cypress it too dominated the valley, the gentle lovely valley which seemed to flow down from a stark mystic birth in the near-and-far mountains of the Abruzzi, a romantic land still if for nothing else than the want of tourists. Even the little railroad was where it should be, in the nearer mountains but on the far side of the main road which in turn was separated from Anticoli by the Aniene. With the river and trees between, together with the elevation, the tooting from the trains and the occasional honking on the highway were no more than reminders of distance, sounds without urgency.

The first night in the cold house Jake slept marvellously well. But to his surprise the morning brought not only contemplation but also anger. The apparent cause of the anger was the regular subdued thudding from painters in the living-room downstairs. But it was more profoundly at Maria, who had provoked their being there. For on first inspecting the house she had acted oddly. She had been delighted with its location – "just right from Rome" – and enchanted by the grounds, but inside she had suddenly folded on the stairwell, slinking down in a corner and saying that the house depressed her, that the bare stone reminder her of Fascist buildings and the nasty brown woodwork of boarding-school. Jake had allowed then for it to be white-washed but he had allowed testily because obviously painters in the house, even some wildflower genus out of Anticoli, were hardly in keeping with his idyll.

"No," Maria had said, "you never really liked the place in town. This is your baby." But the 'your baby' was precisely the trouble because she thought he wanted to get away from the family. This was true even if not in the sense she feared: although he had inconstant reveries they were more controlled than indulged because he knew the consequence of indulgence. He wanted to get away, as Maria also knew, to work. He had never since his marriage worked properly, through no fault of hers surely, but he had married late, he didn't *have* to work and there had been the force of circumstance against his work or to be used against it, Maria's long absence while her mother was so miserable together with her own subsequent illness, all of which had involved him – if anything additional had been needed for involvement – with the children. But the plan for the house had been understood if not stated: it was to be his 'baby' only until he recaptured the rythm of work. With this in mind he had employed the painters to do two rooms as a kind of compromise, not in his heart over-generously, but not aware of so much resentment either. Yet he had thought that Maria might have suffered through her conception of *The House Beautiful* until she herself had got in it.

But Maria of course was only the butt of that morning's anger. For Jake's new contemplation disclosed, again to his surprise, that he had always been angry at someone, at his father for one thing and his mother for another, at a painting instructor for being too rigidly classical or too pressingly modern, at his one-time psychologist first for keeping him on and then for letting him go, at his son for what was perhaps no more than any young male's elbowing, at the most inconsequential people or at any rate inconsequential to his well-being and last but by no means least, only yesterday at Sue, who at six was not so easy as at four. His outburst at Sue had shaken him because in the empty apartment he had suddenly heard himself with the ears of another, remembering too how ugly voices of other parents infuriated him. The outburst, furthermore, had come on top of the *great* incident with Dominique. True, Jake had not – like Dominique – struck Sue, and she was moreover his child – if one subscribed to the strange concept that a parent alone is privileged to abuse a child – and anyway the comparison was absurd. And yet he wasn't so sure that his nasty tone hadn't been worse than a swat on the tail. In any event it had happened.

The strange thing was that to the world Jake appeared a surpassingly gentle man. Perhaps like so many others he had been taken in by the popular opinion and that was why his self-disclosure so surprised him. For there was no doubt about either the depth or the extent of his anger. Even as he faced it lying there, the twittering of the birds exasperated him while one frustrated tree toad – if that were love – was beyond the pale. One could make a scale then from tree toads and inconsequential people through people whom one liked or loved to Tommy, Sue and Maria – in other words there were always motivations for anger. The point was not so much to control it – for on the whole he *had* controlled it – the point was to get rid of it. He was categorically against it as something somehow close to fear and therefore immoral, it was a waste of both time and direction, doubtless too on account of it he didn't paint and anyway, without all these ramifications, he didn't like it.

Very well, he would get rid of it. For regardless of what might be done, of whatever might be the provoking action, if he didn't react then the action would misfire. This was the weapon of saints. Well, other saints had been sinners and he would become one. Not of the Perugino variety with no body structure and eyes rolled in patent ecstasy, but direct, feet firm and with good-will towards man.

Jake's brand-new sainthood did not make him instantly thank God for the raucous display of mating woodpeckers virtually inside his window, but then it didn't have to. He was not aiming to be St. Francis and miraculously or not he ignored the rumpus. Not only that, but on a deeper level he no longer felt anger at Dominique. But this was towards a precipitate solution and perhaps not quite fair to brother saints in general because the strange fact was that he had never felt so very angry at Dominique. It had been like the exception to prove the rule. He wondered why and lying back he wandered passively, imperviously, almost saint-like really over the incidents of that night's party.

He laughed again at what he and Maria had laughed at then, for in putting out Bobby's presents they had both, as if on cue, voiced their misgivings. The trouble had therefore in a sense been foreseen although not of course in the way it happened. In fact they had each meant to get Dominique his consolation prize, but in the country that day with Bobby, Jake had forgotten it and Maria had had so many things to do in addition to the party itself which for some reason never seemed to gel. It had become complicated because Maria had told Bobby and Dominique to invite whom-so-ever they liked, meaning mostly people whom she didn't know in the musical world. But from perversity or discretion, for their Roman concert had for some undisclosed reason been cancelled, they had suddenly decided that they didn't want any of their musical friends. In consequence thirteen more or less hit-or-miss people were assembled that evening for a party which gave every indication of laying a monumental egg.

To begin with the present-opening fell flat. It seemed idiotic – all the Christmas wrappings in April for a so-called adult man – and it messed up the cocktail table making the assembly if possible more mongrel. Moreover the one grande dame who graced the company and who should have brought a present and a big one at that – for she had been invited in good part with this in mind – had misunderstood – or possibly understood too well – for as a niece of a pope she was not only very rich but as shrewd as they come. In any case it was awkward and the lady had to be played up to. All efforts failed. Sue, wound up for the birthday party with a bonus of jumps, was a great help. The plan had been that after the present-opening Tommy should be got off to the movies and that Sue would go contentedly to bed. To ensure this contentment her old nurse, Leondina, had been imported practically up from Calabria and was waiting in Sue's room and willing too, if need be, to stand on her head. No *'beste laide'* plan ever went more dismally astray. Tommy *finally* – after an endless amount of supposedly undercover hints – allowed himself to be led off and although Sue made no public disturbance her sudden controlled tears were a great deal worse for Maria and Jake. They *both* followed her out.

They found her, head bowed, in an attitude very close to *Abject Despair*. But she was talking, not so much to Leondina as to the great wide world and what she was saying made sense: Bobby was her friend also, she had just been on a trip with him where, in Venice and very late too, she had eaten with him every night and now with "the friends", on his birthday and with a birthday cake that she, what's more, had helped Vera bake, she was to be excluded. She didn't quite say all this but there was no doubt about the weight on her heart. Later Jake understood that the scales of sorrow had been tipped by the incident with Dominique but at the time he knew nothing about it or, pope's niece or no pope's niece, he would have reinstated Sue for dinner. Later too, and likewise for the same reason, he understood Maria's annoyance, for without warning she had turned on him, saying, "Let me take this round, please."

What had happened or what had happened from two different points of view had been reported to Maria by both Dominique and Sue toward the end of the ill-fated present-opening. Apparently Sue also had been bored around the cocktail table and had gone into the next room where she had begun banging on the piano. Bobby and Dominique had followed her in – either because of more refined musical sensibilities or in an attempt to save a dying cause – and Dominique had begun to play. ("The first time he touched the piano, I might add, in all the time he's been here," Maria had said later as her indignation continued to mount.) Sue had slapped his hands and he had slapped her.

Where? Dominique had reported on the tail and Sue had reported on the face. Now although the voice of experience might have been heard proclaiming Sue's more probable truthfulness, the fact is that the most skillful prosecutor can find his match in any six-year-old and little girls, moreover, are partial to both drama and embroidery. In any event the next day, after careful indirect questioning, that is, careful not to put the words in her mouth, Sue had said, "No, he just hit me on the behind." That was when Jake explained that although she had doubtless been overboard and troublesome – advising therefore a mending of her wayward ways – the fact remained that it was their house and "the friends" were not permitted to strike her in it and if she wished Dominique would not be invited again. It was then that after one of those moments of childish gravity in which all time appears to have stopped she had said, "Oh he was nice afterwards. He can come."

But that was later. At the time the party, as it turned out, was in no way spoiled. The dinner at the two tables in the little frescoed room, made nightclub-like with candles, was excellent and the Countess Marigny-Sougub, the pope's niece, suddenly shone forth to light up herself and everyone else. Sue, having conquered sleep, reappeared for the cake, and if the incident was to leave a scar, none showed as her face reflected the glory of the candles. Having seen the glory and tasted the cake she went blissfully off to bed. So blissfully indeed that Countess Marigny-Sougub didn't have to stop to punctuate, and therefore, as fashionable people are wont to do – as if for good riddance in one breath both thanking God and congratulating the parents – generously threw into her tales from the lives of the popes, "A beautiful child."

The tales went on over the coffee, ridiculous, fabulous, factual, scandalous, amusing, and then everyone went home happily enough.

76

But the thing rankled in Maria. She said she was angry at Dominique's smugness because when he apologized he had been clever about it; she said she was angry at her own southern training which had prevented her as the hostess from furthering unpleasantness whatever it might be; she said she was angry at her slowness to react. All this was undoubtedly true. But she was angry, as she also said, that anyone had dared to touch her child. "Certainly Sue was probably impossible, but you don't strike a child" and her eyes had filled – "not this one of all children."

"He probably only tapped her."

"Even so," and then for the second time that evening Maria had turned on him. "But I don't understand *you*. You're supposed to be the most protective father that ever lived. Why aren't you het up?"

"I am het up. It's bitter – and after all we've done for them too. The funny thing though is that we saw it coming."

"What makes me mad is that I saw it coming in the car – on the trip. Dominique was starting all those love-pats and I stopped it. I told him if he started, a child doesn't know when to stop."

"He seemed so fond of Sue."

"Oh hell, I mistrust those shows of fondness. It reminds me of your mother with Sue."

"We can leave my mother out of this one," Jake had said happily.

"What I don't understand is Bobby. Afterwards, you know, he backed Dominique up. Do you think there's something between them?"

"Of course there's something between them. I don't mean necessarily physical. But you yourself said when you first heard them play that the wonderful thing besides the technique and intelligence or whatever, is that above the orchestra and in spite of the audience they actually make love to each other. In a way I admire Bobby. He's loyal to his child just as we are to ours. Sure, Dominique's an *enfant terrible* and it must be hard to take. But what if Bobby didn't want to take it, what could he do? They're a team and there's no parallel that I know of, not in business nor with actors or dancers because separately one of them can get a job. Maybe Bobby could be a top concert pianist in his own right but it's doubtful and anyway it's pretty late in the game to try."

"Dominique's enfant terriblism gives me a pain. It's so provincial – always playing the genius and saying that all geniuses are promiscuous. What does that mean, I ask you?"

"The point is, Maria, what do you want to do about it? When they come back I can speak to him or..."

"That's your way. I admit it's more friendly. Mine is to clam up."

"Then clam up."

"Well, we'll see." And then as if the matter were to be closed, Maria had said, "I suppose I didn't say anything really because they're leaving in the morning and it would have seemed petty somehow to have spoiled their last day."

But the matter had not been closed for Maria at all. Jake thought that perhaps in some unaccountable way she had taken over this segment of anger for him.

Yet in the days that followed he thought no more about it because he was otherwise busy, with his sainthood and with his work. They were both coming along fine too although his sainthood, like many another, had its trials. Besides painters in the house there was Antonio in the garden, a simple good man, the perfect strong dumb lay-brother for a saint but needing seeds to plant one day and tools to work them with another, so that Jake was reminded of what he had forgotten: he gave people too much credit. This was again proved in his dealings with the local carpenter, for Jake had commissioned a copy of an ancient work-table the very kind St. Francis might have used, but until he saw the finished product it had never crossed his mind that the man would have cut it on a lathe. Doubtless like all foreigners he was being taken, by the painters, by the carpenter, by everyone who could get a finger in the pie and it was annoying. Still he let it go. He was not going to get angry at so little and he understood why Martins before him had given away their coats and Benedettos their patrimonies. It wasn't so much that it was easier to fit a camel through a needle's eye as the simple truth that if you had nothing there were fewer people around to want it.

78

With a palace apartment in Rome and a two car service about to be running to the country Jake was not quite ready to give his all away, nor could he and at the same time keep his wife, who, although hardly mercenary, appreciated the niceties of foreign living as much as any American who had ever come before her. Perhaps it was better so. Almost any fool St. Simon could wrestle with nothing on a pillar-top or eat traditional locusts and anyway, when you came down to facts, the locust diet wasn't so pure whereas he, St. Jake, was strictly vegetarian if for no other reason than that Antonio's idiot wife could cook nothing but cabbage soup. And as to the wordly goods that he would use to make the ugly house beautiful, well, perhaps he would be the finer saint for them.

A major pitfall on his road to serenity concerned the path leading up to the house. After climbing the hill it clung to the ledge to leave it close by a little hawthorn; then, gently climbing again, it reached the lawn where Bobby had sat that first day. Now Jake had come to love this little hawthorn with an almost Francescan affection. He would sit by it at dusk until the lights, town by town, came on in the hills. The last town's lights made a crown for its peak and in his ecstasy Jake fancied naming it *Corona della Madonna*. The tree likewise had its fleshy side for it is to the hawthorn that Turiddu likens his love in his impassioned overture to *Cavaliere,* and Jake too once long ago had had a Sicilian spring. The tree's buds were firm for promise but it also quite suitably had pricklers on it as if to remind a saint to keep his thoughts up where they belonged.

The drop from the ledge was perhaps some thirty feet with a pile of former years' rubbish below now cushioned by Antonio's yard clippings. On taking the house Jake had been told that the ledge could easily be fenced off. But now Antonio was making difficulties. He said there wouldn't be room for the path without cutting down the hawthorn and that on account of a lateral gully any other plan would be ridiculous because then, after climbing almost to the house, the path would have to descend again. So, after listening to another rigmarole about why the local mason couldn't succeed either, Jake decided to let the whole thing go although he was aware that in this instance passive acceptance was extremely negative because the place was dangerous, not only for occasional visitors but for the children. Still he wasn't going to have his hawthorn cut down, for his sainthood was involved, sitting there by the tree above the ledge.

Sitting there by the tree he also planned his painting. He had to focus constantly because like all moderns he knew too much about a little of everything and as always it was easier to anticipate criticism than to get down to work. *They* would say that his spirit stemmed from Rouault, that the elongated canvas with its frame painted in chiaro-scuro was tricked from baroque, that his technique was borrowed from Roman mosaic or from the rhomboids of early Picasso and so on ad nauseam. Well, to hell with them. So at last he left off thinking to go inside and paint. He painted as if to make up for the long lost time. In cubes of cinnabar to gold he made a flaming frame to hold in his anger, his love, his passion, all to be built in blocks of grey. And what better subject for his confirmation than his new-found self?

As the days and weeks went by Jake continued to paint, to perfect his cubes, to add and subtract until his portrait emerged surer, finer even than he had hoped. But it emerged now not only as Jake. In the eyes, in the hands, in its whole presence there was no denying St. Francis as well. Jake wondered if he was becoming a little screwy.

There were the weekly trips to Rome to steer him straight and there were supposed to have been weekends in Anticoli. But for one reason or another Maria could never seem to make it, using as the final excuse – and often edgily – that as he was working so well she would leave him in peace. On one trip he just missed Bobby and Dominique, who had passed through Rome en route for concerts in Naples and Sicily. Maria was all riled up again.

She said Dominique had apologized, "Oh yes, but not on the grounds that he was sorry, but that he was sorry that he had upset me."

When Jake remarked that this was perhaps a fine line for grievance, Maria – as if having decided against holding back – came out with, "He also gave a lecture on bringing up children. He compared you and Sue to *The Barretts of Wimpole Street*. Did you ever see the play?"

As Jake without undue emotion simply replied that he had,

Maria went on. "That's extremely vicious, if you ask me. Mr. Barrett's affection, you know, at least in the play, made a cripple of his daughter."

Now Jake well knew that a saint-like acceptance of even this statement must be infuriating to the extreme. Yet he still couldn't bring himself to anger, not in this instance because his sainthood was involved, but because he didn't at all believe that his love for Sue was harmful. Therefore, as he said nothing, Maria said, "Dominique did another little turn on promiscuity, adding for my edification, I suppose, that genius is close to madness. What do you think of that?"

Jake thought quite a lot about that. He thought of the eyes of St. Francis in his portrait, that the portrait was possibly finally the work of genius and that Dominique was maybe right. But when he said – this time automatically falling into saintliness – "I feel sorry for Dominique," Maria gave him a very strange look indeed.

Back in Anticoli again with only the so-called finishing touches to do on his portrait, Jake wondered why Maria was *really* so disturbed by Dominique. It was surely no longer the incident with Sue. It was surely too, by extension to himself, in some way connected with the talk about promiscuity. In this vein he wondered if she feared his fondness for Bobby, for it was quite true that he had a Jonathan-like affection for Bobby and always managed, as on that day in Anticoli, to take Bobby and not Dominique – nor for that matter Maria either – away alone. Still he couldn't bring himself to believe that her feeling stemmed from that score.

Nevertheless, he was certain that it was connected with Anticoli. For in speaking of Anticoli the corners of her mouth went in as they did whenever she was hurt and as they had gone in that day on the stairs when, now that he thought about it, she had been the first to label the house *fascist*. This, from her to him, if not a *coup de grace*, had in any case been too close for comfort. Why then had she hit so hard? For if Maria feared promiscuity it was surely more likely in Rome than with erotic nymphs, now long dead, who had once posed for statues in the Piazza Esedra. Or could it be, as often happens, the exact reverse of the medal, not infidelity but fidelity, and was he being altogether stupid? For he was being faithful now

81

not to Maria but to his work. But Maria surely knew that work also had to be flooded with love, otherwise it was nothing. Or at any rate she had known this theoretically insomuch as she had married him not only believing in his work, that is, the painting he had then had to show but, what was immeasurably more, believing in his potential. Could it be that she hadn't understood or that it had only been lip-service and now that he had finally touched the potential she was jealous of it?

It could be too that he was making too much of the whole thing, that from vanity he was over-evaluating the abstinence which perhaps Maria more or less accepted and that it all came down to some absurd little thing such as his having seemingly avoided coming in to meet Bobby and Dominique when they had passed through Rome. So when he next went in he point blank asked her. But Maria had quite openly said, "Oh no, I hadn't even thought about it."

Then he had said, "But I don't want to make an issue of the thing. When they come back up from Sicily I'll come in."

"But you're working," Maria had said. "Why can't they come out to you?"

"Even better," he had said and as a matter of fact they did.

Jake had set the day of their coming for showing his portrait and, almost as eventful, for letting it lay. On the great day, to keep his hands off it, he stretched another canvas. It was a waste of time, preparing his own canvases, but it was his way and while he worked he thought about his next picture. In the same manner he would do Sue – he had put off doing her too long. He would omit the painted frame. It was all right for the Jake-St. Francis, neither good nor bad really, or perhaps the portrait was so good that the frame didn't matter and anyway with his anger gone there was no need for flaming reds to burn it out or hold it in.

He knew exactly how he would paint Sue. Against the grey cubes he would bring out all her round loveliness, Maria's loveliness in essence but with Sue's own wonder added, her particular sensibility and above all her understanding, but also in the arms a nervousness, a tension, almost an awkwardness so strange in such a graceful child and yet perhaps unavoidable now that civilization or life maybe was catching up with her, that its pressures were closing in and the arms were already pushing off what someday must be hard.

Thinking about the picture he forgot the visit until Antonio came up to announce that *"La Signora e qualche Signore"* had arrived in the lane below. Then Antonio hurried down to do the honours.

Jake propped up his portrait where it might best be seen on entering the room. He put his pots and brushes in order and walked down to the hawthorn. It was in full bloom as if to greet his friends.

They were coming up the path, Bobby first carrying several freshly wrapped packages which Jake fervently hoped contained meat, Dominique considerably below and Maria not yet in view.

"The daffodils are gone," Bobby said.

"That was in another month. But my hawthorn is out ... I'm glad to see you."

"Aren't you talking to me?" Dominique said.

"You're not here yet."

Dominique was sweating and panting with the picnic basket. He carried it as if for penance and it was laughable also because usefulness was not his function. As he climbed Jake thought how – under the sweat and the contortion and the wisecracks – he was a very sweet guy and how foolish all the rumpus was.

"I came to apologize and I might as well get it over," Dominique said, sweating also from embarrassment. "Really I'm terribly sorry. It's all so silly because I honestly love Maria and Sue and you more than I can say." In that moment he meant it and Jake loved him back.

"But," and now his eyes shifted to Bobby, back to gauge if Maria were in earshot, to the hawthorn, to anyone or anything that might be party to a crack, *"la folie et la génie sont apparentées, toi, hypocrite, mon semblable* – or, roughly speaking, genius and madness go hand in hand."

"I guess they do," Jake said. He said it like a saint, for who was he to judge? and moreover he was ready to show his feeling Italian-style by embracing Dominique, sweat and all, with his face just there below him. But the set-up was otherwise irresistible.

83

Instead he hit him hard with his open hand.

Dominique slipped and lost balance, his face first unbelief and then horror. For a second he clawed the ledge and then went down still clawing until he hit the heap below. He rolled over – rubbish and all – and then everything stopped rolling except a thermos that went on crazily into the brush beyond.

Jake watched spellbound. Bobby was screaming and Maria and Antonio were running up through the trees. Maria got there first and disappeared into the heap and then she and another lump sat up while Antonio knelt beside them.

"You're insane," Bobby said, white with fear and anger.

"No," Jake said although with a kind of insane pleasure he noticed Bobby instinctively step back from the ledge. He was suddenly furious too. He looked Bobby straight on. "I guess I'm also a genius, that's all." Then he turned and walked up to the house rubbing his hand.

He was thinking of the headlines if Dominique had been killed and of Bobby's subsequent inevitable testimony to the effect that it had been an accident, or of how much worse it still might be if Dominique's hands were injured. He prayed that Dominique's hands were not injured, he knew he should have gone down but he knew also why he hadn't: Dominique didn't matter. The blow had released his feelings and, among them, shame about himself. As he entered the room he saw the silly portrait, silly in spite of the craftsmanship. What a sham his sainthood was, what a sham most saints were too, sluggers who didn't slug but killed the world by denying it, afraid to meet it, to meet man, to take love.

He would have chucked the portrait out the window except he no longer cared that much about it. So he just sat on the bed. There Maria found him. She came in gay as a lark.

"Darling, I knew I had a lot but not this too!"

"Then he's all right?"

"He's considerably shaken as well he might be – great God! He's scratched and his leg's cut but he's sitting up and drinking brandy. He wants a fuss made over him and I for one am going to make it."

"I suppose I should go down.... I will for lunch."

"For lunch! What lunch?" Then she saw the portrait. "Oh

84

Jake, it's wonderful, really it is," and she walked up to it in a way that a few minutes before would have been all that he could have ever wanted. But now the portrait was no more than a period-piece. He was pleased as he might have been by taking her to see a painting in a museum, something done long ago and still far away.

"It's not wonderful," he said.

She came back and sat beside him. "I think it's wonderful, " she said, taking his hand. "Sure... I understand how you feel. But the thing with Dominique is over. It's lucky – a miracle even that nothing happened – but it's finished. So what's the matter?"

"I wanted to be a saint."

She didn't laugh. "Well," she said, kissing the palm of his hand, "you are sometimes. What more do you want?"

"You, I think," he said.

Love and a Walk in Rome

In spite of the apparent disorganization, the lack of discipline and what may well be a love of death, the traffic in Rome has a factory plan. The central piazzas serve as master wheels and the machine belts run out to lesser wheels and so on, into the country.

From the Piazza Venezia one belt runs along the Via del Plebiscito and then feeds back along the Via Botteghe Oscure. To call for Abby at her ballet class, Mr. B. had to cross both streets or face destiny four times. His love of Rome was such that he preferred walking notwithstanding, but his love of Abby was much greater and so, on his days for calling for her, he went by car. One afternoon in March, however, when his wife had not come back with the car, he was obliged to set out on foot. As he approached the first crossing, he thought about awareness and how, although it was something more than a crutch, it was by no means always a cure-all. For he was aware that his immediate danger was not so much from the traffic as from the popular attitude toward it. This attitude was in evidence everywhere – in precipitate crossings, in disregarding rules, in flirting with death. It was a disease that generally afflicted the young male, to such an extent that now, after some years in Rome, when driving and if a boy darted out to whirl with his coat grazing a fender, Mr. B. no longer mentally crossed himself but in sheer admiration murmured "Olé". Yet the disease, like most, had no respect for age and so, even without the juices, he sprinted twice. He made it both times.

Then with relative calm, for no street in Rome is without a traffic hazard, he walked to the back of the Palazzo Doria. He entered the Palazzo through what in its renaissance hey-day had been a vaulted court and was now, to Mr. B.'s shocked delight, a garage. He walked past the cars and up the marble stairs to the ballet class. As he opened the door the same delight was repeated in the damask walls packed with Poussins, all functional with ballet bars.

The class was over, as was also apparently the day's work, for none of the big girls was around, and Mr. B., after greeting the old Maestro, walked back of the screen. Giovanna, the other little girl, was almost dressed but then, as she had a hatchet-faced governess, she had to be. Abby was on the floor struggling with her shoes and as usual monkeying around. They had both been giggling, but when Mr. B. rounded the screen, Giovanna jumped up, curtsied and left. Abby curtsied to the governess and went back to her shoes. She had learned the curtseying from Giovanna and besides the fun of dipping it was a step in wisdom, for the old Maestro was old-fashioned and considered curtseying a sign of breeding.

"Get going," Mr. B. said, "and put on your sweater." He buttoned on her coat, there was another flurry of curtseying to the old Maestro, to his assistant with the elaborate hair-do, to the German boy at the piano, and they walked down the stairs.

"This," said Abby, "is the most beautiful garage in the world."

"As a matter of fact it is."

"I know," said Abby with gentle complacency, "I said it for you this time."

They came into the street and she put her hand in his. It was the old babyhood gesture and with it he always remembered their walks in the woods when she was two, with that wonderful hand even then so personally there, and how, when he would say, "Do you want me to tell you what that spider's doing?", her head would go up and hold, immobile, tense, waiting, enraptured with knowing. She had understood a great deal although she could barely talk, for at about that time, when he had taken her on his lap and told her that he had to go away but that he would come back and that she was not to worry, he had been sure that she had understood, if not the words at any rate the tone, and from it the meaning of promise.

They walked down the Via del Plebiscito to where it narrows in front of the Gesù. There was no let-up in the assembly line. Every so often, when the traffic would begin to drizzle out, a bus would plough up against the stream, and they knew the peril of those buses, for Mrs. B., the year before, while walking with Abby, had been hit. It was a wonder, among other things, that now almost in the exact spot, Abby seemed without fear if not also without memory, and Mr.B. thought of that night in the hospital when, after the pain had been quieted and Liza's leg had been set, she had asked that Abby be brought to her. He had argued that Abby too had had a shock and, as it was late, she would be exhausted, but Liza, against all sense it had seemed, had insisted that Abby "see with her own eyes that I'm still here." It had been Liza, of course, who had wanted "to see with her own eyes" that her child was still there but, no matter the reason, on sight of her mother Abby had burst into tears and sobbed on and on uncontrollably. So, then and there, the fear must have all come out.

The cars came on and on.

"Maybe we'll have to stay here all night," Mr.B. said. "Maybe it'll get cold and dark and somebody'll give us a blanket and then later mommy'll send us dinner and then around midnight..."

"Oh come on, daddy," Abby said. She loved the nonsense but it annoyed her too because her faith had once been so great that it was hard not to go back to believing.

Just then the traffic stopped and they crossed over to the steps of the Gesù.

"Would you like to go in?" Mr. B. asked. "There are a lot of churches in Rome that we can see together. This doesn't happen to be my favourite but it doesn't make any difference. Would you?"

"O.K."

They walked up the steps. They were, Mr. B. thought, about a year or two late. For he and his wife had often worried the problem of bringing up their disparate children in a Catholic country and, some time before, he had suggested that they ought to be taking Abby to visit the churches rather than making a mystery of them or letting their maid take her on the sly. He had told Liza then about Molly Dugan, his nurse in Chicago, and how Molly, after making love with Pat O'Toole on a Saturday night, was too tired for early mass on Sunday and so later, on their morning walks, would sneak him in. He remembered the excitement of a secret from his parents and the feeling of naughtiness and shame too, because he felt that a Jewish boy had no right to be in a church at all.

"It doesn't seem to have affected you though."Liza had said.

"Still waters..."

"But the circumstances were so different."

They certainly were. To begin with, Luke, his son in name and affection since infancy, had been born to his wife by a previous marriage and was as gentile in origin and appearance as they come.

To protect Luke they had taken care through the years not to differentiate between the children and for this reason religion had not been allowed to raise its sectarian head. Or so Mr. B. had always thought. But now, as he walked up the steps, he wondered if his reticence had in any way served Luke, and as for Abby, who was literally being brought up within the shadow of the dome, wasn't it storing up trouble against the evil day? It could be argued that speaking out would constitute a differentiation, but weren't there already all kinds, and didn't his silence really stem from the shame in a church long ago in Chicago? Feelings with time of course change and the shame had long since disappeared, but what hadn't changed was his confusion, for in spite of his assimilation in a Christian world or perhaps on account of it, he had never come to terms with his real feeling about the church until that moment, on the steps with Abby, he realized that the church, regardless of its pronouncements of brotherhood and love, was to him a symbol of humiliation, in essence then a denial of love, a denial that Luke need never know, but that Abby, with her hand so trustingly in his, would someday have to meet.

They entered the Gesù and Mr. B. was surprised to see how at home Abby was. She wasn't awed nor did she put on her foolish smile of embarrassment. As they started up the nave, he again regretted having chosen the Gesù, for he would have liked first to have taken her under the great rose at Bourges or in the apse of Chartres with the jewels of Our Lady bleeding purple from the magic lantern to the stone. The Gesù was a Jesuit church and so in his mind allied with political confessors and persecutions and, perhaps of a piece, here was the golden calf with a vengeance, with one altar, as the guidebook phrased it, "hewn from the biggest piece of lapis lazuli in the world."

They walked toward the high altar but not far. The first two side chapels were dark but on the right, in the third, an electric light cut the gloom. It shone from under an altar on what appeared to be a figure recumbent on its tomb. It was a strange figure, of a priest with hands clasping the scriptures, and it looked like polychrome sculpture. In spite of the glare it was hard to see, for the railing was some twenty feet away and the figure was behind glass. One taper burned on the floor.

"Is he dead?" Abby asked.

"No."

They looked. At a distance the flesh seemed real, even naturally blemished. It could be a dead man and yet Mr. B. thought that it wasn't, perhaps because he didn't want such a gruesome beginning, and, by way of self-assurance, he imagined he recalled that Catholics always kept watchers by a corpse.

"Is he dead?" Abby said again.

"No, he's not dead. He was dead once, of course. That's sculpture. And very bad sculpture too if you ask me."

Abby was spellbound. They were still hand in hand and so, after she had had time to take it all in, he led her away toward the high altar. By way of diversion he explained how churches were usually built in the form of a Latin or Greek cross and then, as they approached the glitter, he thought of Micah and smiled at Abby and, pacing the rhythm, said happily, "Will the Lord be pleased with thousands of rams or with ten thousands of rivers of oil?... And what does the Lord require of thee but do justly, and love mercy, and walk humbly with thy God?"

They had come to the transept and Mr.B. stopped in front of a bust, of a Colonna if he had made out the inscription rightly. "That's sculpture too," he said, "but it's only a head. Of course the other one is sculpture but it's a full figure and it's painted. We can paint something up at home if you like, so you can see for yourself. And..."

"I want to go back and see the other one."

So, no golden calf, no lapis lazuli, no high altar, back they went and stared again.

"As a matter of fact," Mr.B. said, now also spellbound, "his gown is real. It's very strange."

Abby stared for one more moment. "His hair is real too," she said.

They walked out of the church. So it was a dead man after all – if not newly dead then a mummy of some kind. Should he tell Abby he'd been wrong or let it go? She had believed him because at first he'd been convinced. And then later she'd believed her own eyes. Would she forever be confused about death, would death be something dead and not dead, sculpture and not sculpture, something embalmed in a church? Perhaps it was better to think of it that way, with less certainty, without fear.

Outside she seemed quite unafraid, but like him, thinking. He was thinking of his own death, how he didn't want to die until Abby was grown, married or not perhaps, but equipped with what knowledge he had to give and more, the certainty of his love. What then would she think when he died? Of a walk on a cold day and stopping in a church, of something cold like sculpture and yet uncertain, not all dead, like his love still walking with her.

The Kite

In the dawn's early light Nelo reached for his watch, read the morning's first hour and smiled with a satisfaction that is not purely Italian, for the time told him that he had been making love, on and off, for some four and half hours. The confirmation of his prowess had not, however, been his purpose, for he read the time compulsively every hour of the livelong day. With movements as precise and automatic as those within the ancient time-piece, he would remove it from his left trouser pocket, flip the lid with his thumb, note the hour without ever registering any interest in it, close the lid and replace the watch in his pocket. It may have been that the weight of the watch suggested the gold that he no longer had, or that its enameled face reminded him of his elegant origin, but it is more probable that the recorded hour served to assure him that he was still alive, for Nelo was a taciturn and unhappy young man who, until that night, with some episodic exceptions, was not aware of any desire to remain alive at all.

The click-click of the lid was reflected by Paula's eyelids. In that instant she had seen Nelo's smile and misread it, or rather she had read it better than he knew, for she had taken it to mean his pleasure at her being there. From contentment then, as well as languor, she decided against opening her eyes, and, as she was young and very lovely, it was a wise decision.

Nelo's smile broadened, for he suddenly thought how wrong he had been through the years about Veronese's women, because this girl, by both place of birth and features, was a living, youthful Veronese, lush and ripe and yet, as she was so undemanding, not wanton. Of course with the years she might become wanton, but he wondered, on the contrary, if the full-blown women of the canvases, in spite of all the flesh, weren't perhaps passive too, willing and waiting rather than inciting men to pleasure. As he watched the girl, his smile softened, and he was overcome by something close to wonder, for the girl, with her breasts bare and her eyes closed, was incredibly sweet. He took her forearm and kissed it, not purposefully as he had been kissing it all through the earlier evening, and he said again, perhaps for the fiftieth time, "You are so beautiful", but this time his reading was likewise different, for the desire was gone and with it the formula set by an Italian out for "romance".

Paula heard him rightly. Opening her eyes, she smiled and said, "Thank you." Then she said, "I must go".

"Please stay." Nelo was amazed by his own words. After lovemaking, with one exception so long ago that he now sometimes forgot it, he wanted to be alone. He was not always left alone, but until he was it was torture for him, just as any unfinished business was torture, the dishes on the breakfast table until they were precisely arranged, the dishes in the kitchen not yet washed, the time hidden in his watch, the watch opened and not properly closed.

"What would Lella think?"

"What would Lella think!" Nelo laughed the kind of belly-laugh that comes after relief. So Paula laughed too, although she hadn't meant to be funny. She understood, nevertheless, why she had been, because Lella slept almost anywhere. She slept by preference usually with Nelo's friend, George, and, in consequence, the evening had been arranged. What Paula hadn't known was that Lella's promiscuity was common knowledge, nor did she know that the evening's outcome was, in part at least, on account of it. For when, in the late afternoon, Nelo had been invited to make up the party, beyond the fact that Paula was Lella's guest, he had never heard of her, and therefore, in agreeing to go, he had assumed that she would be of the same convenient breed. Although he had been altogether surprised, first by her loveliness and then by her gentle manner, he had been so fixed on the proposition of meeting someone with whom he could sleep for the asking that he never stopped to reconsider it. The faulty premise – and his obtuseness – had in this case paid him well, for it had given him the blind authority that accepts no trifling. Even now, after asking Paula to stay, he didn't see his "mistake" until, when he had stopped laughing, she said, "I only meant, if Lella comes home, she might worry." Then, by way of answering him, she fell asleep on his shoulder.

As long as Lella remained in Rome, there was no problem about

Paula's staying with Nelo. Her mail came to Lella's flat, her parents and her brothers seldom left Verona, and, like them, their friends, following the provincial custom, travelled only in summer and even then not more than a few miles away.

From the beginning at Nelo's, Paula saw little of Lella and nothing at all of Lella and George together. It was not that she wouldn't have liked to; on the contrary, the gradual, forced estrangement from her friend embarrassed her, for she was both fond of and grateful to Lella, and, as to George, she liked him for the simple reason that he was Nelo's friend. Nelo, nevertheless, continued to see George as much as ever, but he disapproved of Lella, not as a person but as a person worthy of his lovely new prize, and, had it not been for Lella's usefulness as a cover, he would have insisted on Paula's dropping her outright. As to Lella in the company of his friend, he was violent, for their presence permeated a sexual aura that, by inference, included his partnership with Paula and was, now that he had fallen in love, intolerable. Not that he was against sex, nor that he and Paula didn't permeate their own aura, but precisely because he had originally mistaken the pattern of Paula's affability, he could no longer bear the suggestion of his happy mistake in others.

As Nelo, with the exception of George, had no intimate friend, and Paula was permitted to see little of hers, they spent most of their time alone. In those first few weeks – and even later – it cannot be said that they were wanting. Nelo continued to work more or less as he had always worked; he was a mural painter, of considerable esteem but in no demand whatsoever, and he spent his time designing either projects that never materialized or, in order to augment a paltry income, jackets for books that he despised. Nevertheless, he accomplished this secondary profession with both precision and taste, even though, as he said, it was absurd, for, "If a book was worth anything, it wouldn't need the sugar coating" and, as a case in point, he would indicate his bookshelf. Although spare, like everything else in his flat – the two Capodimonte cups, the three opaline vases, the black-leather chair, the phonograph on its functional table, and now Paula – it had quality.

Paula, barring one brief interlude, had never worked, and, in consequence, she was almost busy enough keeping Nelo's immaculate flat as she had found it. In the morning, like a housewife, she carefully shopped, buying only what pleased Nelo and exactly as he had instructed her to buy it; later, she would prepare their frugal but always elegant lunch, and then again, usually, their dinner. Of an evening they sometimes went to a film or, even more rarely, to a concert, and on occasion, as a matter of courtesy or duty, for Nelo had little respect for his native contemporaries, to a gallery opening. The structure of their economy, in the beginning at any rate, was not conditioned by necessity because Paula, on leaving home to visit Lella, had been given pin-money. She had also been given, by her father, advice, for he had suggested that while in Rome she might improve her French and English, and, with this in mind, the day before meeting Nelo, she had dutifully enrolled in a course. Now, however, she chose to perfect these languages by buying French vintage wines and choice English preserves, both dear to her lover's palate, and reading the labels aloud, and, as it always delighted Nelo to hear that "It ees our constant endever to present onlee the teenest fruet skeelfullee packed and carefullee selected under the streectest modern and best condizioni nt. wt.3.oz.," Paula, in this specialized field and in no time at all, made remarkable progress.

As label reading, even under the best *condizioni*, has its limitations, after dinner they would climb up to Nelo's terrace where, in the clear October night, when not wondering at each other, they would wonder at the Roman blue. It pleased Nelo then to hear Paula talk, and, as she had little else to tell him she told him of her life; of her lonely and for the most part uneventful childhood in a cold house outside of Verona; of her affection for her father and his devotion to her but of his inability, by either word or touch, to express it; of her mother's stricter encasement, almost as if revengefully locked in herself, and of her brothers' similar remoteness; of how, when she was twelve, she had been sent to the Sisters of Saint Catherine at Mantua, and of her father's instructions on parting, and how, from duty and perhaps also from boredom, she had so carefully followed them that each year, for devotion, deportment and scholastic achievement, she had been awarded *The Blue Star of Merit*; of Lella, whom she had met at the convent and who, although older and of higher station, had become her friend, and how impressed her family had been when Lella had visited her near Verona; of the lethargy and idleness of her life there, later, after her schooling was over; of its almost Arabic isolation relieved only by the one event of the day, her walk at dusk, on her father's arm, to the local bar, bowing to everyone but seldom speaking to anyone; of Lella again, and her seemingly brilliant marriage into a distinguished Florentine family, and how, after the marriage had come to nothing, Lella had periodically rescued Paula by taking her away, and how once, when Lella had thought that she wanted to become an air hostess and was in training, she had invited Paula to Milan, where, due to a sudden emergency and also no doubt on account of her languages and appearance, Paula had been roped in, quickly briefed and packed off as an assistant hostess to Cairo, and how afterwards, although still attending the hostess school on her stop-overs in Milan, she had for some months regularly continued to fly.

From this history Paula omitted two chapters, both in their different ways concerned with love. It may have been that she omitted the first because it seem so inconsequential, or then again because she feared the memory of its magic, like a child's secret, would be broken with the telling. It concerned her love, at the age of eleven, for a peasant boy of great beauty, or it may have been for his kite. In any case, they went together, over the flat lands where the Adige rises in spring, and Paula with them, a trio blessed for the happiness it shed in passing, the boy straight and dark, the girl fair and lovely, and the kite too a beauty. It is unlikely that Paula, from this infatuation, learned any useful lesson about love, but she learned everything about kites, how to cut and bind the poplar shoots, the quality of paper, cloth and twine suitable for different kinds of weather, and, like the label reading or like her deportment in winning *The Blue Star of Merit,* in no time at all she excelled. The idyll with the boy and his kite was over with the summer, for it was at this time, when Paula showed signs of maturity, that her father sent her away to the nuns.

The second chapter Paula omitted intentionally because it would have displeased Nelo, and besides, in telling it she would have felt ashamed. It concerned an affair that had begun on what turned out to be, in every sense, her maiden flight. Her plane, as it happened, had been captained by one Francesco Moroni, an extremely handsome man even as Italian flyers go, who, having caught sight of his novice hostess, was solicitous in every way: his reassurance, in the air, kept her on her feet, and then, after landing, he swept her off them. Although Moroni was both gifted for and experienced in this one-two tactic, what he, like Nelo, hadn't bargained for was the sweetness of his girl. As she was also pliant, he had little trouble in persuading her to continue flying, and, as he was a crack flyer, little more in persuading his company to permit her to. Sometimes she flew to Cairo and back on his plane, but if not and regardless of the place or hour, whenever he telephoned, she would pack her bag and go to him. She went with desire and affection too, for there was something in his dark presence – and perhaps also in his preoccupation with the air – that was reminiscent of her peasant boy and his kite, yet she always went with a feeling of humiliation, for she knew that Moroni had a wife and family, and love in side-street hotels was distasteful to her; and she felt too a kind of hopeless fatality about their attraction, for she knew that of her initiative she would never break it. Moreover she sensed that someday Moroni would, but in this her instinct may have been wrong, for he was – or as much as it was possible for him to be – in love. However, his company acted again, this time against Moroni's wishes, for his expert services were needed in opening a new route in the Far East. He left expecting to be back in a month and expecting too that Paula would be waiting for him, but he was again and again delayed, and Paula read his continual postponement also as an act of fate. In any case, she knew it was her chance and took it. She disappeared, or made herself inaccessible by going home, and she had been there for almost a year when, a few days before meeting Nelo, on Lella's invitation, she had come to Rome.

From Nelo's terrace, that October, there were no black clouds until, without warning, Lella broke the news that she had to leave Rome. As the prospect of immediate separation was unbearable for the lovers, Nelo naturally found a solution: Paula's mail would be readdressed and forwarded by the well-tipped porter. It was so simple that they thought no more about it until, towards early December, Paula had for some days received no word from home. On questioning the porter, she was not only assured, in the manner of Roman porters, that no mail had recently come for her, but that he was stricken that she could think otherwise. The fact was, notwithstanding, that without the reminder of a second tip he had forgotten her, and, in consequence, her mail had been returned. Paula was concerned but she was not kept in suspense, because the next day she received two letters, one from Lella and one from her father, saying pretty much the same thing: her father had telephoned Lella in Florence and had obtained Paula's address, but her father's letter added the ultimatum that, if she wasn't home in twenty-four hours, he would come to get her.

It was of course obvious that Paula's father suspected the worst, but it was also highly probable that he had no proof of it as yet. Paula, as always, looked to Nelo for a decision. She would stay, in spite of her father, or go, if Nelo told her to go. Nelo was torn, not so much between love and duty as by doubt about whether or not his love for Paula, which he had never before been forced to evaluate, was worth the permanent surrender of his heretofore independent, if empty life. He finally not unwisely decided – and, in the long run, not unlovingly either – that only a separation could answer it, but as he hated to tell Paula his decision, he delayed it by blaming Lella, perhaps naturally enough, because his treatment of Lella had precipitated it.

"I don't say she did it intentionally, but God knows she's had enough experience – why couldn't she have misplaced your address?"

"It would have come to the same thing."

"But it would have given us time."

"Why waste what we have on Lella then? It's you I care about."

She was watching him like a child waiting to be told to go, and yet hoping for the miracle of a reprieve, and this made it all the harder.

"The trouble is that I care about you too," he said miserably. "Otherwise it would be easy. But I don't see how, without money,

98

I can tell you to stay, and, under the circumstances, ruin you."

"Then I must really go?", she said, wide-eyed.

"For now. I don't think we have any choice." He took her in his arms, suddenly as brokenhearted as she. "It won't be forever, you know."

Although Nelo missed Paula, he was not at first lonely because he was otherwise occupied. By good fortune an architect for whom he had once repaired frescoes not only commissioned him to paint a small room of his own design, but, while visiting Nelo in order to discuss the project, had admired and wanted to buy one of the three opaline vases. This particular vase was no longer immaculate, for Nelo had painted it, by way of amusement and for Paula's pleasure, with pink and red roses, and it was, indeed, the only material mark ever left by Paula, either during her stay or after her departure, in her lover's well-ordered room. Moreover, she had not left the vase on account of its fragility, but as a talisman that belonged in its proper place, where she too belonged and in the hope that it would bring her back there. Nelo of course refused to sell the vase, explaining that it was no longer his, but he offered to paint another, and, when it in turn was admired by the architect's friends, he painted the third and then bought more and began what he called his "new sugar-coating". This time, however, his bitterness was no more than a carry-over from the prospect of a life spent in illustrating useless books, for while painting the vases he thought of Paula, remembering her praise and how, when he had belittled it, she had said, "I don't see why a still-life isn't worth as much on glass as on canvas." His still-lives apparently were, for, through his architect-patron, they not only brought absurd prices but they also brought him an offer of an exhibition at a fashionable dealer's. When the room was finished, therefore, Nelo had money in his pocket, the expectancy of more and time on his hands, and so he sent for Paula.

She had been only waiting to come, although her leave-taking, as she had foreseen, was painful, for her father didn't believe that she intended to be married, probably because she didn't believe it herself. Her story, in fact, was so unconvincing that she was all the more surprised when, shortly after her arrival, Nelo proposed marriage. As always he ordered the details, in this instance a civil marriage as soon as the law would permit, and he advised her – which in their relationship was tantamount to a decision – in view of her father's attitude, not to write about their plans but rather, a few days before the wedding, simply to invite him. In counselling Paula, Nelo's only purpose was to spare her another scene, for, in his joy at having her back, nothing besides their immediate happiness crossed his mind. He was, nevertheless, aware that for religious ceremonies banns are posted in the birthplace of each contracting party, but, perhaps also because he associated banns with the church, it never occurred to him that the same practice might be followed for civil ceremonies. The consequence of his advice, in any event, was disastrous, for Paula's father had been congratulated, as he wrote her, on his evening promenade to the local café, and, on requesting the reason for this courtesy, he had been informed of his only daughter's approaching marriage. From his parochial viewpoint, he could see only that his daughter had meant to humiliate him, and she had, so deeply, that he promised never to write again.

"Time will mend the hurt," Nelo said not too hopefully, for Paula was really stricken and he was filled with remorse. But she shook her head. "Why take such a grim view?"

"He's like me," Paula said, sorrowfully. "Even though he can't show it, when he loves he really loves."

"Then he should come around."

"On the contrary."

"You can't mean, for your sake, he won't recover?"

"I don't know," she said, looking at him. "But for your sake, I will."

Neither the sanctity of matrimony nor Nelo's modest but promising success immediately affected the newlyweds' lives.

At Paula's instigation they sometimes, though rarely, had guests for dinner, George with whomsoever interested him or the architect with one of his friends, for Paula was ambitious for Nelo's happiness, and, as it now involved his success, she had the foresight to suggest that, with his exhibition in the offing, they should have a coterie of friends "to stand by in the gallery." Nelo of course invited the guests as, by proxy, he selected the food, and although he was always proud of both Paula's efficiency in preparing it and grace in serving it, what pleased him most, as heretofore, was their time together alone.

Since Paula returned there was, nevertheless, one innovation. She had arrived with a huge box that, when unpacked, disclosed, to Nelo's delight, an old, battered kite. He was impressed by her competence in mending it and amazed at her skill in launching it from the terrace, and, as she flew it, he loved her all the more and for the best reasons, because, although he couldn't know it, Paula had brought to share with him the token of her first love. The old kite, however, had seen its best days, and, as Paula had little to occupy herself with in the afternoon, she began a new one, working on the terrace while Nelo worked below. He came up, at regular intervals, to advise her about what he knew nothing whatsoever, and, after it was finished, to paint it. He painted it with the precision and taste that he used for everything else, but as he put into it even more affection than he now gave to his vases, when it was done they were spellbound. He named it, remembering her stories, *The Blue Star*.

The new kite flew higher and better than the old one. When on clear nights, Paula flew it, to Nelo she was the wonder of the world, a *donna mobile* in every sense, as pale as death when her kite was in danger, flushed and exultant when it went free, and altogether assured as the kite took wing, as if the air were her element also and she was at home in it, for then, suddenly, she knew all its markings, the stars and the planes and the strange bird's cry. As he caught her ecstasy, he told her of his love, and although fine words came hard to him, he called her his Lady of Verona, the shameful mistress of the air and of his heart, and he told her too, for he was aware of his despotic ways, that theirs was a marriage of the humdrum earth and the open sky.

The kite-flying was, perforce, discontinued as the evening of Nelo's exhibition drew near. With this great event in mind, Nelo had bought a piece of brocade, of a kind that in imitation of Renaissance splendour is still made by hand in Italy. Although from its price it might have been cloth of gold, this particular piece was off-white with little pink and red roses in the fabric, and Nelo had been unable to resist it not only because his painter's eye told him that it would set Paula off to perfection, but because its colours, as if by design, simulated what had become the stable colours of his vases. It was, as he knew, a wildy extravagant joke, but when Paula appeared dressed for the exhibition, he thought he had carried the joke too far, for she seemed to him so altogether lovely that only a fool would look at his vases.

Paula was, indeed, admired, but so were Nelo's vases and, more important, many of them were sold. When the crowd had gone and, at last, Paula and Nelo left the gallery, they had every reason to be happy and they showed it. As they stepped into the street, the light caught Paula's hair and dress, and she, in turn, the eyes of the men passing by. One of them did more than stare; he stepped and called, "Oh Paula!", and there in his uniform, as splendid in his way as she, was Captain Moroni. Although in greeting her, he did not use the familiar *tu*, his manner said as much and more, but even if Nelo could have missed it, Paula's lovely skin told the story. She had turned marble white, then blushed deeper than the flowers in her dress and white again before she could stammer, "Oh – Franceso – Captain Moroni – this is my husband." The men did not shake hands because Paula had already turned away, and so Nelo turned to follow her.

As he caught up with her, it began to rain. He opened his umbrella and put his arm around her, and, huddled together, they walked the short distance home. It was not a position conducive to conversation, nor did he want one. He had been startled but in no way upset by the meeting, for he had never assumed that Paula's stories were complete, nor had he ever valued what he thought of as a peasant's price on virginity. He had been struck most of all and naturally enough by the Captain's movie-star physique, but, perhaps also naturally enough, he had been flattered by it, and, as he walked through the rain, he smiled, for he thought that if this Captain exemplified the past that Paula had renounced for him, he must be pretty *formidable*. All in all then, with his exhibition under his belt, as he shook off the rain and turned on the light, he was feeling fine. He was all the more surprised, therefore to see that Paula was still disturbed. In order to relieve her embarrassment, he asked, casually enough, "Who was that character?" and, when she said, "Oh, someone I knew in the air service", he only added, "I daresay."

As Nelo soon forgot or at any rate dismissed the Captain from his mind, so did Paula. In the days that followed, he was occupied with his show, particularly in the late afternoons when he often stayed on in the gallery until closing time. Meanwhile Paula, with nothing else to do, went back to her kite.

One afternoon when the wind was high, she had trouble landing it. In consequence, when Nelo came home from the gallery, his dinner was late and he was annoyed. He knew that he should not be annoyed and he knew, furthermore, that as Paula in order to please him was always punctual, his annoyance was unreasonable. Nevertheless, as he heard her pottering around the kitchen, his annoyance increased, and he asked himself why in the name of all that is holy, with the entire afternoon to fly her kite, shouldn't she have his dinner ready? At that moment, unfortunately, what he took to be the answer came to him. Indeed, it suddenly seemed all too clear. For in their months together, Paula had never flown her kite alone on the terrace, nor, for that matter, in the afternoon, and then, the day after meeting Moroni, she hadn't been able to wait – nor, from the singular evidence of the late dinner, could she bear to part with it. It fitted too well: her love of the sky, her interest in planes, and he remembered with mortification how, as if out of the mouth of a babe, he had called her "the mistress of the air and of his heart." Perhaps, for all he knew, in the not so distant past, Moroni had left *his* mistress of the air, but, if he had, it was apparent from the way he had looked at her that he now wanted her back. Not that what *he* wanted concerned Nelo. It was what she wanted, and in thinking of her sweetness to him, he tried and would have shaken off the nightmare had it not been for what seemed to him the irrefutable proof. For now that he associated the kite with Moroni, he not only recalled at their meeting the testimony of Paula's sudden pallor followed by the quick flushing, but he reinterpreted it, not as

103

embarrassment but as excitement, for wasn't it in precise duplication of her ecstasy with the kite? Worse still, even though he could hardly bear to think of it, she had never shown these colours for him.

Nelo said nothing to Paula at dinner. Indeed, afterwards, he hardly spoke to her. As the days went by he still tried to throw off the indignity of his jealousy, but then he would turn sick again in thinking of her tell-tale skin. He did not ever permit his fantasy to go beyond what he understood to be the facts, for he never believed that Paula had been unfaithful nor that she even knew the significance of the kite. Instead, perhaps like all men who have loved and been betrayed, he reworked the parts into what seemed to him the most unique and bitter irony. For as he reasoned, if Paula had a flesh and blood lover, it would be one thing, to face and deal with even if he lost her, but a phantom-lover was beyond his or any man's reach. It was, moreover, precisely the illusive aspect that made speaking futile and the heartbreak so poignant, for, if he spoke and she denied it, what good would that do? And, if the phantom had always been between them in her desire, hadn't their love been a sham?

Meanwhile Paula could not know what she had done. She was certain only that the late dinner was not the root of all their misery, because, as she could with affection enumerate Nelo's faults, she knew that pettiness was not one of them. She would have guessed that the trouble lay in the meeting with Moroni, and she often considered it, but because after the meeting and until the ill-fated dinner, Nelo had been, if anything, more ardent in his affection, she found no clue. There was nothing for her to do but what she had always done, please Nelo as best she could, and, as her presence was apparently distasteful to him, whenever possible she got out of his way. Under the circumstances it was the worst thing she could have done, for there was no place to go except the terrace, where whether she flew her kite or not, Nelo thought she did. Indeed, a less disciplined man would have broken sooner, for as he imagined that her phantom now so bewitched her that she could no longer resist it, the sounds on the gravel above him were like the turning of a screw.

As time went on Paula flew her kite almost constantly, but no

104

longer so much from habit as in hopelessness, and so listlessly that one afternoon she almost let it go. Instead she decided to speak with Nelo, because her instinct told her, even though she couldn't substantiate it, that the trouble went back to the meeting. It was a difficult decision, not only because she was uncertain, but because their conversation, at least in the days when there had been any, was always initiated by Nelo. Nevertheless, when dinner was over and after she had brought his coffee she stood next to him and said, as if reciting, for she had rehearsed it, "Perhaps it doesn't matter, Nelo, but I want you to know something: I haven't seen Francesco Moroni except for that night with you, in almost two years."

He looked her straight on. "Yes, it matters very much. It would have been better for all of us if you had." He said it in despair, but his anger, at the mention of Moroni or from the release of words, was about to burst. It did after Paula had gone up on the terrace, for she had just launched her kite when Nelo was beside her, his face white with fury. He screamed at her to pull it back, but even before the kite had reached the parapet, he was tearing it apart. He had become ugly with the violence, but what horrified Paula was the kite, for as he ripped it and its segments dangled from his hands, she had the strange and awful feeling that she was witnessing the dismembering of her own body. She was so faint and ill that she didn't hear the pieces of the kite as they fluttered to settle in the court below, nor did she know that Nelo had turned and left her on the terrace. So it was no wonder that no one ever knew whether she, who had always been so quick to please him, fell or jumped to where her kite lay broken.

Laura

Tony picked up the mail that had been shoved under the studio door and put it on the table. The room was insufferably hot. He opened the window and the door onto the terrace. Outside ... from somewhere by the sea ... the evening Roman breeze was on its way. He unwrapped his painting and put it on the easel. The spot of vermilion was just right. Before he'd broken with Vera he'd done nothing like it ... she'd been so negative about his painting the wonder was he could paint at all. But why had he wasted all that time with an old woman who'd never shown him? And she'd got everything she'd wanted out of him

He turned over the mail. He was pushing thirty-eight ... he'd better pull himself together. Old Risi'd been right : a painter worth anything found a milieu that helped his work. With all the people who'd wanted him and with all the affairs who'd ever helped him? Only Zio, who hadn't wanted him at all. But with Zio he'd have had to go on painting under pressure .. all those long dreary hours. What he needed was someone rich enough so he could paint when he wanted to.

In the mail the bottom envelope was from Vera's gallery. Inside there was an announcement of the show with a clipping. The last sentence was underlined: *Anthony Marotta, an American painter of Italian descent, the one newcomer on the Roman scene, is represented by three paintings of such quality one wonders why they were relegated to the back room of Vera Brann's gallery.*

He read it again dumbfounded. Vera had put him in the show! It could only mean she wanted him back. Or had she included him because Zio had bought so many? Either way with that notice what if they were sold?! Then would she take him, not for her lover .. he couldn't take that again .. but like her other painters whose success she'd made? One thing was for sure: whatever happened he wasn't going back to restoring frescoes. But what then? He'd have to find someone else.

It was the show's last day but there was still time to go.

He walked to the back room and, yes, there were his paintings and a girl looking at one of them so intently she hadn't noticed him. She was probably an art student, she was dressed that way in denim with a shoulder bag .. but no, there was an air of elegance about her with her high-heeled shoes, perhaps to give her height. She had wonderful dusty red hair and under the denim the promise of a beautiful body, and her bearing was particular too. He stood watching her; part of the pleasure was her immobility, as if she too were spellbound. She didn't know he was there .. but, yes she did .. she turned and smiled. She was very pale with no make-up and very beautiful, her green-blue eyes touched with the dust from that hair. He'd never seen such a girl and yet there was something familiar about her. Then it dawned on him. She was Zio's daughter!

She'd been in America at college and her mother .. hadn't Zio told him? .. had been American. If he spoke English to her he'd give himself away .. "Ti piace?" but he shouldn't have tutoyed her.

She giggled. "Molto."

"Is my Italian that bad?"

"Your English is better." He was incredibly handsome, like an advertisement in his white silk turtleneck and blue flannels. "I love the painting .. those mystic blues... it's as if I'd been there."

"It's not a real place."

"Oh I wasn't in a real place. It's magic, isn't it, the way he knows about atmosphere?"

"How do you know so much about painting?"

"I don't .. I know about air and the wind. The wind's in all of his, even when it's died down. I love everything about his painting, even where he puts his name .. in this one in the cloud. He's wonderful, isn't he?"

"If you think so."

"That's a funny thing to say. Don't you think so too?"

"As a matter of fact I do .. or did. And now I do again."

"I'm enchanted."

"I am too."

"Do you know Marotta?"

"Yes."

"Tell me. What's he like?"

"You tell me."

"You're Marotta!" and she laughed, delighted that this tall, dark, wonderfully charming man was the painter her father had discovered and surely he must have charmed her father too.

"They're about to close up here. Let's go and have an espresso, shall we?"

In the piazza the tables in front of the bar were crowded. "I don't really want a drink, do you?" the girl said.

"Shall we walk?" They turned toward the Tiber. They had to wait for traffic before crossing to the steps down to the river. It was high with derelict wood and other spring debris. Overhead the clouds were running too, dark cumulus against the fading sky. There was no one else on the quay.

He took her hand. "I like everything about you!"

She smiled and looked up at the sky, her eyes wide with wonder.

"What do you see? Air and the wind .. is that how you know about them?"

"From flying kites. On a day like this I used to fly them."

"Alone?"

"With the boy who lived in the villa next to us. We flew everywhere on our magic carpet. Oh look! that cloud's like yours in the painting. Your name should be in it."

"What's yours?"

"Laura."

Yes, Zio's Laura .. without Zio's knowing it and after his break with Vera .. it couldn't have been better .. this girl who had everything and beauty too. His fate was there for the taking. "Tell me about the magic carpet."

"Oh I always wanted to fly."

"Is it so bad down here on earth?"

"Does it mean that? Well, so did Aldo, the boy with the kites. At my grandfather's in Siena once he got me to try in a glider. He'd had it made for him. He almost killed me."

"Was that Aldo Aldobrandi?"

"Do you know him?"

108

"In Rome his name's like Rockefeller. I didn't know he was that bad."

"My father thought so. He stopped my seeing him."

"Was that at one of your mother's or father's places?"

"My father's. It's so beautiful, the Tuscan land. I was brought up there. Do you know it?"

"From the painters!"

"Oh I knew that from yours." The lights came on across the river. It was getting dark on the quay. "Your landscapes have the same distant magic the masters put in theirs."

"I knew you knew about painting. Only you and Risi, my maestro, ever said that. I love you, Laura." He kissed her. "Now you can believe me."

"I'm not so sure."

"Let's see." They kissed again. "Yes, you can." But he was afraid he was pressing too hard. He moved as if to stand up.

"Tell me about you."

"What do you want to know?"

"Shall I begin? Born in New York, awarded scholarships at art school. You won a prize at the Carnegie. After you came to Rome you restored frescoes at the Palazzo Chigi. Why'd you do that?"

"To eat. Doesn't the catalogue say that too?"

"It doesn't say anything personal, nor about your family."

"My parents are teachers, both born in America. My grandparents came from Lucania. And I have a little sister about your age. She has red hair too, not like yours, bright red. In Lucania there are children like that; they say it came from the Normans."

"Then for a while you were only child too. Were you happy?"

"More than most. They always made me feel wanted."

"How wonderful to be loved like that."

"It taught me how. I'll teach you."

"Were you ever married?"

"I never met the right girl before. Let's."

"But you don't know me."

"Enough to know I want to be with you always."

"I want to be with you too, but I've known you longer .. from your paintings my father has and the ones in the gallery .. I've gone to see them every day .. they tell everything about you."

"I love you, Laura. My parents were married after they'd known each other only two days and they didn't have any money either, and it's the only good marriage I know. Let's get married tomorrow."

She laughed. "You can't in Italy. Banns have to be posted."

"Is there no other way?"

"I don't know it. If there is my father will, though."

"Let's not spoil it, darling, by telling anyone. Or do you feel you have to?"

"It will be hard for me not to.. we've been so close. We'll have to anyway sooner or later."

"Later then."

The last of the afterglow streaked the sky. The river caught it and on what had been the black water the clouds were mirrored by the moon. Then the magic drifted downstream as if taken by the current and it was dark.

"I don't want to leave here ever."

"The miracle wasn't the reflection on the water .. it's us, Laura, feeling we belong to each other."

Zio picked up the framed photograph .. Constantia with Laura on the beach at Sabaudia .. both so lovely. Laura had been nine then, the year Constantia died. It had never occurred to him to remarry. He'd tried to make it up to the child .. God knows he'd understood her loneliness. With the years she'd grown more like her mother. Poor Constantia, known everywhere at Laura's age as the great heiress .. with her father's fear of fortune-hunters she'd thought no one would want to marry her except for her money. He'd spared Laura that ... and Zio smiled. She wasn't even aware of the fortune that would be hers.

Zio looked up at Tony's painting .. it had never had any business there with his fine paintings. He'd have it taken down in the morning .. only his indolence had kept him from having it removed with the others. He wondered again how much his loneliness after Laura went away to college had come into his having seen so much of Tony. He'd been flattered, he had to admit, by all of Tony's attentions even though he'd known he'd been wasting his time, and Zio laughed .. he was rid of him. He was happy Laura was home again. Not that he'd seen much of her lately. It was unlike her to stay out all hours without telling him. Well, she'd graduated from college, she was no longer a child. He hoped she was having a good time.

The intercom sounded. Now why would Tony come to his office except to sell him a painting? He couldn't face another. His secretary opened the door and to his annoyance Tony embraced him.

"My!" Tony was looking at the paintings and smiled as he saw his. "I'm in good company."

"Why have I the honour of yours?"

Tony sat on the desk. "You'd better sit down too, Zio. I'm in love with Laura. We're going to Scotland to be married. Why don't you come with us?"

Zio was overcome. He couldn't speak. So that was why he hadn't seen her. And Laura had told him nothing.

"I thought I should come to prepare you. We met in Vera's gallery."

"And you knew she was my daughter?"

"It was because she was your daughter I couldn't help falling in love with her."

"You fall in love conveniently."

"Until I met Laura I was never in love with anyone."

"How often do you say that? It's out of the question. You made an unmistakeable suggestion to me, and now are you telling me you're normal for my daughter? With your two minds about sex, what kind of happiness would Laura have?"

"You don't know anything about sex, Zio. And you've got it all wrong about me. My pattern emotionally has always been with women."

"It's not possible."

"How can you say that? When you married your closest friend's daughter?"

"Go away for a year. Go away until you find out how you stand. You can go where you want. I'll finance you. It would give Laura a chance to find out how she really feels too."

Laura opened the door. Before she could speak Tony kissed her.

He patted her behind. "Where'd you get the jeans, darling?" Over them she wore a purple shirt that with her dusty red hair accentuated her pallor. Zio's heart melted. She was so young and beautiful. But there was something different about her.

She embraced her father. "What did you do with Tony's paintings?"

"I had them up for a time."

"Why are you here, Tony? .. Well, if you won't tell, maybe Zio will."

"I'm old-fashioned, darling. As his prospective son-in-law I wanted your father's blessing."

"You told him!? And you made me promise not to!"

"If it was a mistake I'm sorry."

"And another mistake, Laura, would be to marry in a hurry."

"Zio wants me to go away."

"What is this? Are you two deciding for me?"

"Nothing's changed, darling."

"Then you didn't tell him I'm pregnant?"

Zio looked at Tony. "So it was all planned and calculated."

"I always thought you'd be so happy with a grandchild. Do you want me to have an abortion?"

"These days people don't marry because of a child."

"When they love each other they do." Tony put his arms around her. "Who could help loving her?"

"With your technique you mean who could help being seduced."

"You've never talked this way to anyone. Weren't you and mother happy when she was having me? Why shouldn't we be?"

"Your mother and I were very much in love but we didn't have a child without planning for it. There was little similarity, Laura. I could support her. I not only never wanted her money, I never used it. She knew she could trust me."

"He means me, darling. Well, if I can't convince him I can you." He kissed her on the mouth, holding her close as if he meant to make love there and then. As he let her go his look to Zio said, "You see I've won."

112

It was late and as Zio had hoped there was no one in the gallery. Then Vera came out from her office. She was tightening the belt of an old raincoat; with all her money she never bothered with clothes.

"Well, stranger,*benvenuto*. I've really missed you. Shall we go in my office?" and as he followed her, "I see your enchanting grandchild weekends on the beach at Sabaudia. How long since you've seen him?"

"Too long. I came back this morning. Laura telephoned me to come."

"I'm surprised you didn't come before."

"I felt too defeated, Vera."

"What keeps you in America?"

"I'm considered an authority on Italian Law there .. I have many friends."

"You have here too. You and your daughter were always so close. With my children I went to the other extreme. I can't say it came out any better."

"I thought my being away would be better for the marriage."

"Did you really think your absence or anything else could change Tony?"

"I hoped the child would."

"From my experience a child never solved any parents' problem, surely not Tony's. He wants excitement or he's bored with no matter whom .. Risi, me, you or your daughter. No one ever has enough to offer .. Well, we both learned one thing from him: a young lover or friend doesn't make one young again."

Zio smiled. "I never thought so, Vera."

"Well I did .. from the moment I met him. Risi brought him to one of my seminars, and with his charm and that presence he made me believe" .. she laughed .. "and at my age too .. that he was interested only in me."

"A predator who's just sighted a victim, why wouldn't he be? Which is not to say, Vera, he wasn't enamoured too."

"Tony was never enamoured of anyone but himself. But he can be so ingratiating he's hard to read. I think I came nearer to love with him than with anyone. I always wondered why you stopped seeing him."

"Because he was too ingratiating."

"With you of all people?" She smiled. "Tony's sex, I'm afraid, is conditioned to people he thinks can be of help to him. His principles .." she laughed .. "if you can call them that .. didn't bother me. It was his painting. Except when you asked me, in all the years I've had galleries I've never exhibited anyone I didn't believe in. He left me because I wouldn't handle him. He'd have left me anyway of course. Why'd you buy so many?"

"For the same reason I urged you to include him. I thought I'd seen a gift that if encouraged would come out full bloom."

"He doesn't believe in his own gift .. or he'd work. He never has .. with his looks and charm and his attraction to wealth .. from an immigrant family how could he not be? And he was always afraid of being poor. He told me. But after what you knew, how bitter you couldn't prevent her marrying him."

"I should never have hung his paintings with the others. When Laura saw them she thought I believed he was a great painter, and then when she met him .."

"My dear, Tony never needed any help, when he turns on that charm, selling himself to anyone ... For a man like that a woman has to be tough, or tough and old like me."

"I didn't know how I'd failed her until it was too late .. and she'd gone."

"At that age they all want what they want when they want it. Why do you feel so guilty?"

"It wasn't Tony alone. She was so vulnerable, Vera. She didn't know about the fortune that would be hers. And with no mother to help or warn her .. or prepare her .. I never said a word to her about sex."

"Whatever you'd have said would have been wrong. Listen, with all the mistakes I made with my children I'm in no position to tell you about yours. Except I know this: we weren't interested enough or too interested in ourselves .. or in our own importance .. it's the same thing. Call it what you want .. we didn't give it. And then we're disappointed or hurt with the result."

"What aren't you telling me?"

"Didn't your daughter tell you why she'd called you? When Aldo Aldobrandi's not at your villa, Tony's at his. It's common knowledge at Sabaudia."

"You make me sick. I'm going there tonight."

"I am too. Can I take you?"

"That Aldo, even when he was a boy, was vicious."

"Surely you know more about these things than I, but are you going to the villa alone?"

"With whom should I?"

"Even though your daughter .. with my old history with Tony .. might not like it, I'd be better than no one. The villa's so isolated and with two of them it might be awkward after dark."

From the beach he could see the lights from the lamps on the terrace and all the old pleasure in that beautiful house came back to him. They were probably still at dinner. Zio slowly walked up the steps.

Tony was sitting between Laura and a man. In the half light Zio couldn't really see him.

"Daddy!" Laura got up and embraced him. "How'd you come that way?"

"I walked from Vera Brann's. She brought me. I'm staying there."

The men had got up. Aldo had been a handsome boy but Zio hardly recognized him. He'd never seen a man so bleached, so tanned and with so much gold on him, medallions and chains.

"You must be tired, darling."

"Not from the walk," Tony said. "Welcome."

"You remember Aldo."

"How is your father?"

"I don't know." Aldo and Tony laughed. "He's due here."

"So is this." Tony had taken champagne from a cooler. Next to it Zio saw two empty bottles. Tony popped it. "In your honour." He brought Zio a glass and filled it, then Aldo's and his. "To you."

"To Peter. He must be a big boy now."

"He's a wonder."

Aldo laughed. "But no governess yet. I was just telling Tony all the ways we had of getting rid of Laura's. Which one did I get to?" He laughed again. "Oh yes, the best. That was when Laura'd say to

115

me, 'You're lucky to have a mother'and she'd cry for real. That's what made it so good, and I'd say to the governess,'Look what you've done to her."

"I never knew all the trouble I was making for you, Daddy, until you were asking a governess to stay and I listened at the door. You didn't say a word against him or that it was my fault too. All you said was, 'The boy's mischievous but her only companion here.' And she said,"Laura looked at Aldo, "Better no companion to corrupt her. He's not mischievous, he's vicious!"

She must know, Zio thought. Tony filled Aldo's glass and his.

"And you said to her then, 'The child's lonely. Try to be more affectionate.' I was so moved with your protecting and loving me that when you came out I kissed you and cried and you comforted me." She kissed her father. "I've missed you so much."

Aldo stood up. "Laura wants to be alone with her father. Let's go to my place."

"Stay with us, Tony. I came to see you too."

"Wait for me up in the studio," Tony said.

Zio looked at him and then at Aldo. There could be no doubt that what Vera had said was true.

As they started out Aldo stumbled and laughed, "The old man'll think I'm drunk."

"Must you leave, Tony?"

"I'll be back."

Laura stared after them. Zios' unhappiness for her was almost more than he could bear .. if only he'd never laid eyes on Tony.

Then Tony came out carrying the child. He put him in Zio's lap.

"Such a fine boy. Peter, darling" Zio whispered. "He has your beautiful complexion and your hair, Laura."

Peter stirred.

"I want you to see his eyes."

"Tomorrow I will. Let him sleep."

Laura picked him up and went in.

"Sit down, Tony. Does this .. your friendship with this man .. mean your feelings for Laura are over?"

"What makes you say that? You know I always wanted to be your friend. It was because I couldn't be, really because Laura was

116

your daughter I fell in love with her."

You bastard, Zio thought, you'll try anything.

"Yes, I had a liking for you too, up to a point, and bought your paintings so you'd have money. That's what you liked about me."

"How can you say that?"

"Not only me .. Vera, your marriage, and now Aldobrandi. You're got up very handsomely. But what about my daughter? In that baggy dress .. don't you even allow her enough money for a hairdresser? And no nurse. Why?"

"That's the way she wants it."

"I failed her, that's certain, not warning her about your proclivities."

"It wouldn't have made any difference."

"It does now. If you don't care that the whole village knows of your homosexual activities, we do. I can do nothing about that but there's one thing I can do and will: stop the cheques I send here."

Tony smiled. "But it's her money," and he stood up.

"When I'm dead it will be. If you're counting on her grandfather's estate, Laura doesn't come into that for another ten years."

"Laura never said that."

"She didn't know. Have you forgotten she's so young? Or do you think that's why she accepts this humilation? I won't permit it any longer. Until this has been cleaned out and there's proof of it, not one more penny. But it's your decision. Aldobrandi's enormously rich, in his own right I believe, so if you choose him there should be no problem."

Tony seemed to have disintegrated. He looked at Zio and went in. The only thing that impressed him, Zio thought, is the money. Zio heard him go up the stair.

"What do you think of your grandchild, Zio?"

Laura sat beside him. "He's enchanting now that he's beginning to talk. You'll have to stay for him." Zio took her hand. "He needs your love too." She broke and went on sobbing. "I'm so miserable .. help me .. what did you say to Tony?"

"That this can't go on. Why didn't you ever tell me, honey?"

"For so long I didn't know. I always hoped he'd change and

come back to me. What could you have done about it anyway, daddy?"

"I can take you away now, for a while anyway. It'll give you time to think .. and Tony time too. If he loves you, he'll come after you. It's not final, darling. The whole world's before you .. you're young and so beautiful."

"Tony'd never let Peter go."

"With your unhappiness this is no place for the child, and with the Aldobrandi villa here, whatever happens, there'll be no end to your humiliation."

"I'll think about it, dad. I'll talk to him again."

"Not when he's drinking, and certainly not, darling, when that Aldo's around."

"I'll come back and say goodnight. I can't see my life without him."

"He thinks he's so irresistible he has the right to everything, and he's taught you to believe it."

She went into Peter's room, kissed him, and then into theirs. As usual Tony wasn't there. It was later than she'd thought. In the mirror of her dressing table she looked like she felt; with no help .. Tony kept all the money .. how could she look differently? Zio was right .. why should she take this? Suddenly she was furious at Aldo. She wouldn't stand it any longer. She ran out and as she went up the stair she heard them. Then what Zio had said about talking when Aldo was there came back to her. She didn't care, she didn't care about anything but to *get Aldo out!* At the top of the stair the door was half open.

"I'm fed up."

A glass broke. Aldo laughed. They were drunk. "Who wouldn't be with her. She was always a Christ-bitten bore."

If she could kill him .. she started to go in.

"And stupid." She stopped. Tony'd said that!

"Why you fell for that spoiled bitch is beyond me."

"I never did, really."

If the bannister hadn't been there she'd have fallen. It wasn't only Aldo. What was the use of going in, of talking, of anything?

"In vino veritas. Let's go. Have you got your passport? Here's your gun."

"Don't point it at me."

"Don't tell me again you're not coming because of the boy. You use him to blackmail me .. that's all you like about him."

"I'll tell you something, Aldo. In all my life I never felt affection for anybody but him and you. Funny, it happened at the same time, when he was born.

It was more than she could bear. "Get out."

"Look who's here."

"You, Aldo, get out! Both of you get out! And you .. you, Tony .." Then she saw the gun. Tony saw that she saw it and reached for it and as they both grabbed it it went off.

She fell and lay there blood streaming from her head.

They stared at her. Then Aldo, neatly avoiding the blood, stepped over and went down the stairs.

Photo: George Peine

III

Poems for Children and Others

The Dugone

the dugone is seldom seen by the upper gentry
for it lives in a dugout under the sea
it's a kind of a fish, yet it suckles its young
which can't be much fun for the baby dugone
for whenever he wishes one of those dishes
so loved by young fishes he finds that the juice
from the dug or the pap or the tit isn't much use –
in fact it ain't fit – he don't like it a bit –
as the salt from the sea has turned it quite stale

the same might be said for the young of the whale.

The Amoeba

Ages after the world began
But long before the time of man
Some six hundred million years ago
After the fire had died, in the afterglow
When the ice had melted and the pristine snow
Had gurgled and oozed into mud below,
An animal in all its prime
Rose up from the primeval slime.

　　　　To understand its life and scope
　　　　One needs to use a microscope.

Even so, one's so small
It can't be seen at all.
It's called AMOEBA HOTTENTOT.

Another kind God then begot
Is called AMOEBA GARGANTUAN.

Both are superior to man.

Why?

1. They do not befoul their living-place.

2. They have no need to prowl in outer space.

3. They are not vexed with sex.
   When they wish to reproduce
   They cogitate, "Now what's the use
   Of all the fuss?" And, without more ado,
   They simply split themselves in two.

4 They are
   By far
   The oldest animals that are.
   And wisdom (ha ha) comes with age.

Kindly turn the page.

The Dino

the dinosaur
does not exist anymore

from the tip of his tail
to the end of his nose
was longer than you would suppose

how far?
not quite so far as the nearest star

although he was immense
he was dense
he had a pea-brain and made no sense
and was a scare-cat too

when he lived there was not yet man
but had there been I think you can
imagine what he would have sung
as he rocked to sleep his little one

> Listen, babe, don't be afraid
> There ain't no dino in the shade
> And if there were and you said, "Boo",
> He'd scuttle right away from you.

My Doodle Bug

My doodle bug
Has a lovely rug
But what is in her noodle?

Her rug is red
With dots of black.
It's on her back
And there's a crack
For wings.
And with her legs
And other things
She sings.
But oh so softly
That only other doodles
Who are near
Can hear.

(What you hear from a thicket
Is her cousin, the cricket).

When my doodle bug
Opens her rug
To fly away
I don't cry.
I know she's going
Away
Somewhere in the sky to play
With another doodle –
Or maybe with her poodle.

My doodle bug
Has a lovely rug
But what is in her noodle?

Kutzu

Kudos for the kutzu
the only animal who
has horns that seem to flow
a beard that shouldn't grow
and stripes as white as snow

question:

> with attributes so few
> why praise the lone kutzu?

answer:

> a creature in the zoo
> no less than you needs cheers
> to alleviate his fears

Chitin

What the hell
Is chitin?
It is somethin'
Fittin'
Like a glove
From above
To below
On grasshoppers
That hop
On bottles
That go pop
On fireflies
That glow
On any bug you know –
On any bug that's flyin'
Or any bug that's sittin' –
It's a bug's skin
That's what's chitin.

The Oneger

The oneger is a wild ass
Are you one?

        To roam the grasses,
Munching and making passes
At other wild asses' lasses
Must be fun.

        For a while anyway.

Still I wonder, oneger,
If to be stung by gad flies, not in the mind,
But on your behind, isn't a bore.

You can't even smile. You can say Hee-haw
But, pshaw, you haven't much choice.
Like me, a tame ass, you have hardly a voice.

Puthytails at Fothenfire

Puthytails, puthytails, where have you been?
And hath god wrought your fluffineth
More thenthetive than lovely puthies are themthelves?
And if tho why
Mutht thome poor guy
Letch and cry
For open thighs
When me, oh my
Along the path that thkirts the thea to fothenfire
Are myriads of puthytails for his poor heart's desire?

Hubris/Chutzpe

hubris is chutzpe
only it's worse
chutzpe is bad enough
hubris's a curse.

as for example:

say hubris met chutzpe
walking down Second Avenue
and went up to chutzpe
and said, "Bud, you're a Jew."
that wouldn't be hubris,
that would be chutzpe.

or again:
say chutzpe met hubris
somewhere in the Isles of Greece
and went up to hubris
and socked him in the teeth.
that wouldn't be chutzpe,
that would be hubris.

a culture with roots
so hostile and polar
sooner or later
had to be over,
i.e.,
it was fated to fall,
and it has.
                    That's all.

Stephen Blake

A kittiwake
Called Stephen Blake
Was infinitely shy.

For when dining in some gay café
Or lolling on a crowded quai
If he perchance heard some bird say,
"Who is that handsome guy?"

The reply would be
Inevitably
"A kittiwake
Called Stephen Blake."

Then, after a pause, the prurient bird,
Would likewise be overheard,
"A kittiwake!
Called Stephen Blake?
But Kitty stands for girl."

Poor Stephen Blake
How could he take the inference
With just plain indifference?

My Love

my love is like an octopus
    clinging
my love is like a nightingale
    singing
my love is like a bell
    ringing
          all for you

Broom

1
I gathered broom
For Granny's room

2
She layed her head
Upon the bed

3
I gathered broom
For Granny's tomb

Tell me anything

Oh little flower in the earth
Tell me how you came to birth.
Was it like the friendly wasp
Or like a baby in the hosp?

Tell me what your mother found
Sleeping there upon the ground
All round and small and smooth and sweet,
A little bud called Lil or Pete?

Or were you like a waspy's runt
A-stingin' everything it shoun't?
Or was it more like mine found me,
A-yelling to beat jimminee?

And tell me then when you arose
To face the day without your clothes,
Can you remember back at all
When you were too so very small?

Oh little flower in the earth
Tell me things about your birth.
Or if you can't remember that
Just tell me anything.

Never say Downy to a Brownie

(song for Brownies)

never say DOWNY
to a BROWNIE
for it's UP UP UP with us girls
with our hair straight or in curls
we will use might and main
and never spare pain
to do goo-oo-oo-ood
as we shou-ou-ou-ould.

or if we should fail
we'll not cry nor bewail
for we always can sing
of one certain thing:
Oh JOY oh JOY oh oh JOY
there never was a BROWNIE BOY.

Could it be the ear?

1.

According to a press report
The Queen of England took a snort
Of late with the Austrian minister
Of state. Nothing prime nor sinister,
Just ordinary diplomatic,
Yet the press was so ecstatic
and the Austrians so elated
That the nation celebrated,
All because: the Duke of Edinburgh,
Helping his Queen up from the mall – on the Thames –
Up the steps to the banquet hall,
Lined with Austrian retinue
(Quite a few in all – including dames),
Was said to have said – he came to a stop –
Before greeting his host who stood at the top,
Prince Emil-Ludwig Schnauzernott,
"Meine Damen und Herren, grüss' Sie Gott!"

2

Had it only been so. What princely finesse,
What a noble show of delicatesse!
What reasonable reason for general elation
That the consort of the ruler of a once mighty nation
Had stooped from his height only to please
A tiny nation from over the seas
(And likewise the Prince, who came up to his knees);
Had he only said nothing else but,
"Meine Damen und Herren, grüss' Sie Gott!"
It would have also been spectacular
For his precise use of Austrian vernacular.

3

What happened was this: the Queen's couturier,
Gigi Jean-Gourray, became a cropper
And, to sauve qui peut, told a whopper;
In fact he downright lied
Assuring the Queen that the tulle
On the nether part of her derrière,
Exactly where it seemed to pull,
Concealed the royal backside.
Of this misfit the Duke was unawares
Until, after the Queen, he started up the stairs,
When he did *not* say, aloud, up from the mall,
"Meine Damen und Herren, grüss' Sie Gott!"
But sotto voce, in an Oxford drawl,
"Mine own dear heart, hold in your butt!"
"Grüss' Gott! Grüss' Gott!" came the joyful replies—
The Austrian corps was in paradise.

4

The Austrian press, it is true, implied
More than "Grüss' Gott" might have signified,
As if a special rapport with the little nation
Could have relieved the whole world-situation.
Still it makes one think, not only about hips
And dressmakers, but of what's behind the slips
Of our policy makers, about Rusk's and McNamara's positions—
Are they due only to inordinate ambitions?
For with Boa Dai, Diem, Khanh and now Ky,
There must be something more than meets the eye.
Could it be the ear? Perhaps every time
There's a blunder, one of them's primed
To allow, sotto voce if not in an Oxford drawl
Yet somehow loud enough to be heard by all,
"LBJ, you're a wonder."

Notes do not a themy make

notes do not a themy make
nor apples raw a pie

to make a pie
one pares the fruit
then seasons it

to write a theme
first have a scheme
reflect a bit

one kneads the dough
and moulds it for the pan

so likewise you before you cook
take up your pen, take out your book
and formulate a plan

The Boys are Talkin'

The boys are talkin', Daddy,
 Down in the village square,
They talk a' things in gen'ral,
 An' a-happ'nin's "over there".
How every father's laddie
 Does long to leave his hoe,
And every fellow down there –
 Tells how he'd love to go.

They say ol' man Cotler's boy
 Was shot dead, like a spy –
They stood 'im up against a wall,
 He never winked his eye;
His dad comes up to me an' smiles
 And says that "some day, too,
Your dad'll have as good a
 Chance to be so proud a' you".

The boys are talkin', Daddy,
 Down in the village square,
They talk a' things in gen'ral
 An' a-happ'nin's "over there".
Now will you promise, Daddy,
 That when I'm eight and ten
You'll let me sail f'r "over there"
 An' join our fightin'-men?

May 6 1918

Sand-lilies

I know
Where the sand-lilies grow.
In the dog-day heat
They're as white as snow…

I should have been a florist.
My mother, a post-Victorian lady
With many gifts
Few developed and none disciplined,
Knew a great deal about flowers
And I learned, unawares in Michigan,
Where to look
And how to pick
And put and tend.

Now here in Italy –
(after half a century)
On this ancient inland sea
Eleanora Croce came to call on me
And said, "Ah, sand-lilies,"
Naming them botanically,
"Very rare, so they say,
And *unico* to this *sezione,* by the way"
And went on to talk of German poetry.

She, like her father,
And her sister
And her daughter and her son,
Perhaps unto the fourth generation,
All write,
For they too learned unawares,
Which may be the best way
And why I,
Thinking of Vietnam
And of the lilies that somewhere

Must still grow there,
Can write no more than,
"You, Mr. Johnson,
Will never know
Where the sand-lilies grow"..

Italian Trees

The planes in rows along the European waterways
Are Sycamores.
In Rome they pull away from progress,
Arms mutilated like other arms by wires, fires.
The trunks grow straight
But seem to bend as the branches tend
To where the river flows,
Falling free but sometimes hardly normal
As the lovely sprays fall, fall over the walk and wall
Lower even than where the trunks begin.
These river branches form a vault
More devious than any man-made barrel.
For promise they sprout little yellow flowers
And bear too, caught in their intricacies,
Dirty testimony of man's perforce indecencies,
Worn love, old blood.
Yet the vault can hold its own
With others local groined ribbed or cloistered
Both younger and older and less original
Against the sky on rainy nights in spring
Its lacings make the heart cry out
For beauty wanting and in pity,
For under it poor lovers come
Supporting desire along the balustrade
Wrapped so richly unto themselves
That they can shed time, weather
And the touching world of other loves and lovers,
The hunted trapped to hunt the hunters.
They are Italian trees and lovers
Living and letting live
So long as extremities still meet
Or do not fall too far below the root.

142

Yes and No

Put the books in the stacks, but how?
Topically, linguistically,
Chronologically, alphabetically?
There is so much that I'd have liked to know.
Are they a record then, with the dust,
Of wasted time? Yes and no.

Stewing

The worst of neurotic abuses
Is to stew in one's very own juices.

Go Browse in Clover

Youth now is over
Go browse in clover
Call not old Rover
He lies long buried
Why do you worry
No need to hurry
Your time will come

A Mirror for Virginia

These jewels are fake and not worth much
Until like me awakened by your touch
As the cold cold glass is quite devoid of grace
Until quickened by the loveliness of your face.
And if the loveliness is underlined in lines
Around the eyes for love and friendliness,
Around the lips for sensibility and, alas,
For disappointment and a fear of emptiness,
Do not despair. Know that where the glass
reflects the beauty is relatively thin;
It lies there but also deeper and within.
The lines are drawn to tell the years
In which you, my dear, dared take of life
As befits the courage of my wife.

A Christmas List

I made a Christmas list
And now many of my friends are beginning to die;
My wife's one-time almost lover
Who lived entangled with his mother
In a great house on a southern hill
Just like it has been written about so much
– She lived on pride and morphine and such
My old friend, Alfred,
Who never quite made it
And yet had a warm heart and hot body too
With his warm heart and hot body
And the dreams that never came true;
And Joe, the banker, with his cold banker's ways
Who would have liked something else
But never would permit anything besides
A certain percentage.
Yet these three, like others,
Saw the tide roll in.

Sister Pain

Sister Pain, Sister Pain
Please go out into the rain.

Sister Pain, have a heart
Stop kneading on the smitten part.

Sister Pain – oh sweet shit –
Sister Pain, come off of it.

Photo: Philip Wilson

Well, Tania, Farewell

Well, Tania, farewell.
This is our second leave-taking.
We said goodbye last spring
In Rungstedlund,
Where I had come with the insane idea
That you might give me your gift;
But you couldn't or wouldn't
Or I couldn't take it
In the cold stone house by the northern sea
With the warmth of your open-armed welcome inside
Even though, I think, it was coated in anger
Not at me
But at the effort my being there involved.

In the beautiful rooms you gave me
I felt I should be both younger and older,
An eighteenth century gentleman –
With a servant somewhere in the courtyard –
Writing his memoirs.
I write them now.

We talked
First and least about your furniture,
Which was the loveliest I had ever seen,
Fashioned perhaps after illustrious English cousins,
But more personal, for it was handed-down,
And more colorful, in northern fruit and pine,
And friendlier too
As if the cold sap elegantly encased,
Like yours, was warm inside;

And about the dinner that it pleased
Your constant fancy to pretend
Was scheduled in my honour, although we both well knew
It was for the new ambassador.

149

The dinner, the last perhaps you gave,
Was, as planned, a beauty.
There were ten of us in all
And I remember how we gentlemen
Paraded, to my delight, in old-world fashion
In the candlelight, each with his lady.
On my arm there floated – hardly touched –
Your niece, "the last of the précieuses",
As you had twice forewarned me
So that I might rise and shine.
But alas, as always, I was tongue-tied.
The lady, however, deigned to drop one pearl:
While I was looking across the table
At you, sparkling with elegance and ear-drops
And hospitality too,
Painted, I suspect, against pallor and for bravery,
And yet so very ill and frail,
The lady caught my look. I said,
"My! you Danes have courage."
"My aunt went to Africa a Dane,"
Said she, "and came back a Masai."

Later we talked again, vaguely of politics,
And you said the old order had gone out
And that if socialism couldn't hold the line
Communism, just across the border, would come in
And that you, if you lived, would stay to see it,
But that your friends were horrified
And had ships in readiness to take them – where?
Over the sea is ever the land's fairest way.
Then you told the story about your aunt,
Somewhere in the land in another great house
Spending her days tending geese,
And how terrified she was, for them too, of communism,
And how one day you said to her,
"But you, aunt, have nothing to be afraid of,
For if the commisars come, they will make you head goose-woman
Of Denmark

150

And give you a car with a driver
And you will ride throughout the land inspecting geese."
Then you laughed and said.
"I think I made the old woman very happy."

I wish I could have made you happy.
I think you were when we talked about Rome
And our friends and my family there
And particularly about Haidee;
You pressed me for every detail about her
And as I told you I wondered
If it was because she too, like you,
Has a magic, although of a different kind,
Or if because my child in some way represented
The one thing you had perhaps always wanted and never had,
Or, more than that, if it was simply her childhood
With the vitality of the promise
That you were clinging to.

You clung to me too, for the same reason,
And came out into the court
And leaned for support against the doorpost
To wave goodbye. As I drove away
I thought of that other time
In Denmark
When we rode out to the cottage in Dragør
And you, bandaged and so terribly ill,
Were carried down the clapboard stairs by a fisherboy
For what? To greet us and give us tea.
Even your courage
Must have at the end been weary,
But I think you would not like to be remembered wearily
But nobly. You will be.